ASIAPAC COMIC

C000214472

THE YELLOW EMPEROR'S MEDICINE CLASSIC

TREATISE ON HEALTH AND LONG LIFE

黄帝内經

Written by **Zhou Chuncai**

Illustrated by **Zhou Chuncai, Han Yazhou, Han Yi & Hou Xiuqing**

Translated by **Wang Xuewen & Sui Yun**

ASIAPAC • SINGAPORE

Publisher
ASIAPAC BOOKS PTE LTD
629 Aljunied Road #04-06
Cititech Industrial Building
Singapore 389838
Tel: (65) 7453868
Fax: (65) 7453822
Email apacbks@singnet.com.sg

Visit us at our Internet home page
http://www.span.com.au/asiapac.htm

First published December 1996

©1996 ASIAPAC BOOKS, SINGAPORE
ISBN 981-3068-28-0

Cover design by Marked Point Design
Body text in 8/9 pt Helvetica
Printed in Singapore by
Chung Printing

Publisher's Note

As a publisher dedicated to the promotion of works on Chinese culture and science, we are pleased to bring you this graphic presentation of *The Yellow Emperor's Medicine Classic: Treatise on Health and Long Life.*

Regarded as the highest authority on traditional Chinese medical knowledge, the treatise is based on the philosophy of yin and yang and the five elements. The theory of this ancient medical knowledge is exerting an increasing influence even in the scientific world today.

To enhance your appreciation and application of this volume, a list of essential terms is appended for your easy reference. The original text in the Chinese classic is also included to complete this rendition of the treatise.

We would like to take this opportunity to thank Zhou Chuncai, Han Yazhou, Han Yi and Hou Xiuqing for their lively comic illustrations. Our thanks, too, to Wang Xuewen and Sui Yun for translating this volume, and the production team for putting in their best effort in the publication of this book.

Essential Terms

Hanyu Pinyin	Chinese	Meaning
bagua	八卦	eight-trigram
bi	痹	numbness; rheumatism
bing ding	丙 丁	the third and fourth of the ten heavenly stems
danzhong	膻 中	chest centre
fu	腑	lower internal organs
geng xin	庚 辛	the seventh and eighth of the ten heavenly stems
hun	魂	ethereal soul
jia yi	甲 乙	the first and second of the ten heavenly stems
jin	津	saliva; sweat
jing	精	zygote; essence of life
jiufeng	酒 风	literally meaning liquor wind
keqi	客 气	vital energy in the universe
kui	葵	a kind of vegetable
laoli	醪 醴	undecanted wine
liangyi	两 仪	duality; yin-yang
lingshu	灵 枢	miraculous pivot
mixian	麋 衔	a kind of medicine
po	魄	corporeal soul
qi	气	vital energy; energy of life
ren gui	壬 癸	the ninth and the last of the ten heavenly stems
sanjiao	三 蕉	triple burner
shen	神	spirit
shuxue	俞 穴	transport points
sixiang	四 象	four states
suwen	素 问	plain questions
wu ji	戊 己	the fifth and sixth of the ten heavenly stems
wuji	无 极	null state; infinite state
yang	阳	the masculine or positive principle in nature
yang qi	阳 气	masculine energy of life
yi	意	intention; wish
yin	阴	the feminine or negative principle in nature
yin qi	阴 气	feminine energy of life
zang	脏	upper internal organs
zhi	志	will; aspiration

Contents

Huang Di, or the Yellow Emperor, is generally regarded as the ancestor of the Chinese race. Among his many important contributions to the Chinese people, the compilation of the medical classic, *Huang Di Nei Jing*, or the *Yellow Emperor's Medicine Classic*, is a shining example. Legend has it that he lived to the ripe old age of 117 and was on the throne for a century. Because he practised the policy of benevolence, the officials and the people got along very well and the country enjoyed abundance and prosperity.

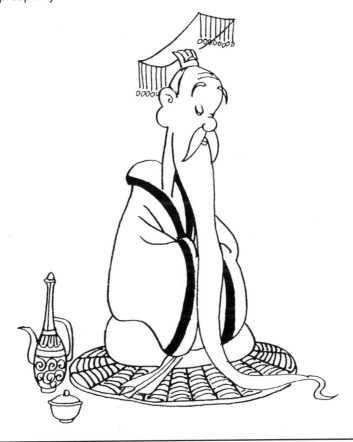

Origin of *The Yellow Emperor's Medicine Classic*

In his infancy, the Yellow Emperor was very clever and quick to understand things.

He had high analytical powers and was good at making generalizations.

On the left are herbivores, and on the right carnivores.

After mounting the throne, he developed science and culture to a higher level, thereby laying a sound foundation for the Chinese system of thoughts.

The theory of this Rubicube is found in the book Luoshu.

Compass

Carpenter's square

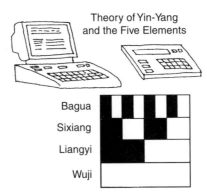

Theory of Yin-Yang
and the Five Elements

Bagua

Sixiang

Liangyi

Wuji

Comprehensive and profound, his theory still shows a great potential and an increasing influence even in the scientifically advanced present-day.

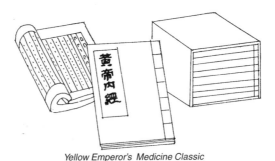

Yellow Emperor's Medicine Classic

The Yellow Emperor's Medicine Classic, completed with his direct and indirect participation, is based on the philosophy of yin-yang and the five elements. An important part of his theory - prevention as the major way to good health - deals in detail with man's lifestyle, eating habit, physical and mental health.

Interaction between Man and Nature

The Chinese way of maintaining good health advocates that man and nature are interactive. Since its birth, the earth has been revolving round the sun while rotating on its own axis. Since his birth, man's autonomic nervous system has been directing the functions of his various organs.

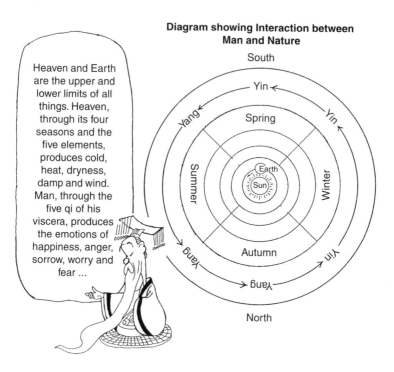

Diagram showing Interaction between Man and Nature

Heaven and Earth are the upper and lower limits of all things. Heaven, through its four seasons and the five elements, produces cold, heat, dryness, damp and wind. Man, through the five qi of his viscera, produces the emotions of happiness, anger, sorrow, worry and fear ...

At the centre is the sun around which is the earth's orbit.

The third ring from the centre shows the positions of the heavenly stems.

The fourth ring shows the names of the 28 constellations.

The fifth ring shows the names of the 24 solar terms as well as the position of the earth corresponding to each of them.

The ancients put the three yin and three yang on an imaginary orbit in the direction of the arrows, advancing one step each year (one revolution every six years). It is called the flow of keqi.

The 12 "Officials" (Organs) of the Body in *The Yellow Emperor's Medicine Classic*

*SUWEN

The Yellow Emperor

Qibo

Qibo was reputedly a physician and an official of the Yellow Emperor's. He is referred to as Heavenly Master in *The Yellow Emperor's Medicine Classic.*
The classic is divided into 18 scrolls and 162 fascicles. It comprises Suwen (nine scrolls) and Lingshu (nine scrolls). Suwen is on the theories of maintaining good health and treating diseases.

* Suwen means plain questions.

Treatise on the Natural Truth in Ancient Times

There is a kind of inherent vital energy in man. The principle of maintaining good health is mainly about the preservation of this vital energy so that it is not wantonly dissipated.

原文：帝曰：余闻上古之人，春秋皆度百岁，而动作不衰。今时之人，年半百而动作皆衰者，时世异耶？人将失之耶？岐伯对曰：上古之人，其知道者，法于阴阳，和于术数，食饮有节，起居有常，不妄作劳，故能形与神俱，而尽终其天年，度百岁乃去；今时之人不然也，以酒为浆，以妄为常，醉以入房，以欲竭其精，以耗散其真，不知持满，不时御神，务快其心，逆于生乐，起居无节，故半百而衰也。

The Yellow Emperor: I hear that most people in ancient times lived over 100 years and remained active and healthy. But nowadays, people become decrepit and failing when they're only 50. Is it because of changes in the environment, or people have neglected the way of maintaining good health?

Qibo: The ancients who knew how to remain healthy followed the principle of yin and yang and lived in harmony with nature. They were moderate in eating and drinking, worked and rested regularly and never over-strained themselves. So they enjoyed good physical and mental health and lived to a deserved, ripe old age of more than a 100. But nowadays people don't behave like this. They drink wine like water, live recklessly and indulge in sex even after becoming drunk. Their passions dissipate their vital energy, so they become old and decrepit by the age of 50.

But now people don't behave like this ...

Physiological Stages in a Woman's Life

原文：肾者主水，受五脏六腑之精而藏之，故五脏盛乃能写，今五脏皆衰，筋骨解堕，天癸尽矣。

At 7: begins to grow permanent teeth

At 14: begins to menstruate

At 21: becomes fertile

At 28: muscles and bones are strong

The kidney rules over water, receives and stores essences from the viscera. Only when the viscera are full of life and vigour, are they able to discharge the generative essences. As the viscera decline with age, the generative essences are depleted ...

At 35: face begins to wrinkle

At 42: hair begins to grow grey

At 49: menopause

Physiological Stages in a Man's Life

At 8: begins to grow permanent teeth

At 16: becomes fertile

At 24: attains peak of fertility

At 32: bones and muscles are strong

At 40: hair begins to drop

At 48: face becomes sallow

At 56: vitality wanes

At 64: teeth begin to drop

原文：夫上古圣人之教下也，皆谓之虚邪贼风，避之有时，恬淡虚无，真气从之，精神内守，病安从来。是以志闲而少欲，心安而不惧。

Ancients well-versed with the way of self-cultivation said noxious influences and evil winds should be avoided and people should remain tranquil in heart and rid themselves of all sorts of greed.

Evil Winds
虚贼邪風

Then the vital energy in their bodies would always be in harmony and be well preserved instead of getting dissipated. So, how could they fall ill?

Wah ...

They exercised restraint of their will and had composure in mind and tranquillity in heart, without cravings, and without fear.

I have found it!

原文：形劳而不倦，气从以顺，各从其欲，皆得所愿。故美其食，任其服，乐其俗，高下不相慕，其民故曰朴。是以嗜欲不能劳其目，淫邪不能惑其心，愚智贤不肖不惧于物，故合于道。所以能年皆度百岁，而动作不衰着，以其德全不危也。

With their spirit in harmony and everything in proper place, they toiled but didn't become too weary.

They were not choosy about their food and clothing and were happy to go along with customs. There was no envy at others' positions. Everyone lived a simple life.

Their lifestyle conformed with the principles of maintaining good health; that's why they could live 100 years without becoming decrepit.

They shunned unhealthy habits and were unswayed by evil lures.

Whether they were stupid, clever, virtuous, capable or otherwise, they had no fear of anything.

原文：帝曰：有其年已老而有子者，何也？岐伯曰：……男不过尽八八，女不过尽七七，而天地之精气皆竭矣……夫道者，能却老全形，身能虽寿，能生子也。

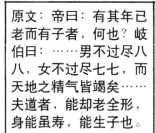

Some people remain fertile even in old age. What's the reason?

Generally, fertility won't last beyond the age of 64 for a man, and 49 for a woman.

But a man who knows the way to maintain good health is able to conserve his vitality, remain in a vigorous physical state and maintain his fertility even when he's old in years.

Going by physiological calculations, a person's normal life-span should be between 120 and 150 years. So, one must first overcome the psychological barrier of premature senility.

The spiritual men

The sapients

I've heard that there were four types of ancients who knew profoundly the way to maintain good health.

The sages

The worthies

13

Treatise on the Harmony of the Qi of the Four Seasons with the Human Spirit

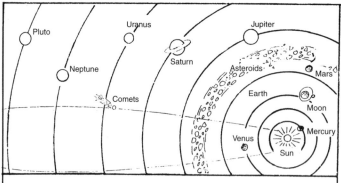

原文：天气
清净光明者
也，藏德不
止，故不天
也。天明则
日月不明。

The qi of heaven (dynamic energy) is pure and bright. The heaven is always there in motion since it conceals its virtue and brightness. Otherwise, the sun and the moon would not have been shining as they are.

Then noxious qi would sneak in; the qi of heaven would become clogged up; rain and dew would not descend and there would be no intercourse between heaven and earth.

The four seasons are characterized by growing in spring, strengthening in summer, harvesting in autumn and storing in winter which are also characteristics of the qi of the four seasons. The key to good health is to harmonize one's spirit with the seasonal qi.

The resulting disharmony between yin and yang would stifle life; even sturdy trees would wither inevitably.

The three months of spring are the season of renewal for all things. With everything flourishing, the world is full of life

原文：春三月，此谓发陈，天地俱生，万物以荣。夜卧早起，广步于庭，被发缓形，以使志生，生而勿杀，予而勿夺，赏而勿罚，此春气之应，养生之道也。逆之则伤肝，夏为寒变，奉长者少。

To accord with the season, go to bed a little later and get up a little earlier.

Let things grow and do not harm them; give and do not deprive.

Go for a stroll in the courtyard, loosen your hair, relax your body and freshen up your mind.

This is the way to cultivate the qi of life in spring. Violating it will result in injury to the liver and lead to illnesses of a cold nature in summer, making the body less capable of adapting to the flourishing qi of summer.

Enjoy the season and do not do anything harmful to your health.

The three months of summer are the season of luxurious growth. The heaven qi descends and the earth qi ascends. All things become fruitful with the intercourse of the two qi.

原文：夏三月，此谓蕃秀，天地气交，万物华实。夜卧早起，无厌于日，使志无怒，使华英成秀，使气得泄，若所爱在外，此夏气之应，养长之道也。逆之则伤心，秋为痎疟，奉收者少，冬至重病。

To accord with the season, go to bed late and get up early; do not grumble about the long, hot summer day.

Stay cheerful and do not get angry.

Be as lively as a blooming plant to keep the yang qi in your body in good circulation.

This is the way to adapt to summer and nurture the "growth qi". Violating it will result in injury to the heart and lead to illnesses such as malaria in autumn. It will also impair the ability of the body to adapt to the "collection of qi" in autumn and lead to relapses of illness in winter.

The three months of autumn are the season for harvest. It is getting cooler with the winds blowing stronger. The qi of earth is clear and everything changes colour.

原文：秋三月，此谓容平，天气以急，地气以明。早卧早起，与鸡俱兴，使志安宁，以缓秋刑，收敛神气，使秋气平，无外其志，使肺气清，此秋气之应，养收之道也。逆之则伤肺，冬为飧泄，奉藏者少。

Go to sleep when it is dark and get up at dawn, just like the rooster.

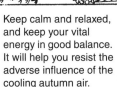

That is the way to adapt to autumn and nurture the harvesting qi. Violating it will result in injury to the lungs, leading to indigestion and diarrhoea in winter and weakening the capability of storing in winter.

Keep calm and relaxed, and keep your vital energy in good balance. It will help you resist the adverse influence of the cooling autumn air.

Ah-choo!

17

The three months of winter are the season for closing and storing, with rivers iced over and land frozen with cracks.

原文：冬三月，此谓闭藏，水冰地坼。无扰乎阳，早卧晚起，必待日光，使志若伏若匿，若有私意，若已有得，去寒就温，无泄皮肤，使气亟夺，此冬气之应，养藏之道也。逆之则伤肾，春为痿厥，奉生者少。

Do not disturb the yang qi in this season. Sleep early at sunset and get up late after sunrise.

Let your spirit be as calm as if it is in hiding; and as if you have some

private matter to keep from others. Remain happy and contented as if you've come to know a secret.

This is the way to cultivate the storing qi in winter. Violating it will result in injury to the kidneys, leading to flacidity in spring and reduced capacity to adapt to the flourishing spring qi.

Avoid the cold and keep warm. Do not let the skin perspire to prevent the yang qi enclosed within from being affected.

原文：逆春气则少阳不生，肝气内变；逆夏气则太阳不长，心气内洞；逆秋气则太阴不普，肺气焦满；逆冬气则少阴不藏，肾气独沉。

The liver is the organ with the general's position. Those going against the principle of keeping in good health in spring will not bring to life the lesser yang qi. The subsequent penting up of the liver qi would result in illness.

The heart is the organ with the monarch's position.

Those going against the principle of keeping in good health in summer will not have strong greater yang qi, resulting in illness caused by weakness in heart qi.

The lungs are the organs with the premier's position.

The kidneys are the organs with the position of the official of labour.

Those going against the principle of maintaining good health in winter will not be able to store the lesser yin qi. This would result in illnesses caused by weak kidney qi.

Those going against the principle of maintaining good health in autumn will not be able to collect the greater yin qi. This will result in heat in their lungs, manifested in panting and chest congestion.

原文：夫四时阴阳者，万物之根本也。所以圣人春夏养阳，秋冬养阴，以从其根，故与万物沉浮于生长之门。逆其根，则伐其本，坏其真矣。故阴阳四时者，万物之终始也，死生之本也。逆之则灾害生，从之则苛疾不起，是谓得道。道者，圣人行之，愚者佩之。

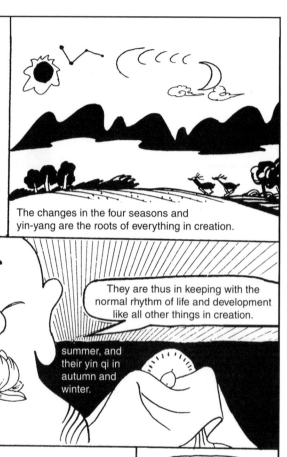

The changes in the four seasons and yin-yang are the roots of everything in creation.

They are thus in keeping with the normal rhythm of life and development like all other things in creation.

The sages conserved and nurtured their yang qi in spring and summer, and their yin qi in autumn and winter.

Those who go against these changes that govern growth, experience decline followed by death.

Those who go along with these changes would remain free from illness, for this is the way to maintain good health.

The sages follow the way to maintain good health but the ignorant often go against it

20

原文：恶气不发，风雨不节，白露不下，则菀槁不荣。

Vegetation would not flourish in an atmosphere of noxious air with wind and rain out of moderation and white dew failing to descend.

There would be evil winds and a deluge of rain; the order of nature and the seasons would be disrupted, resulting in the premature deaths of living things.

原文：贼风数至，暴雨数起，天地四时不相保，与道相失，则未央绝灭。

原文：唯圣人从之，故神无奇病，万物不僻，生气不竭。

Only the sages could adapt to changes in nature and were therefore free from strange diseases. If all living things could do likewise, their qi of life would not be exhausted.

原文：从阴阳则生，逆之则死；从之则治，逆之则乱。反顺为逆，是谓内格。是故圣人不治已病治未病，不治已乱治未乱，此之谓也。夫病已成而后药之，乱已成而后治之，譬犹渴而穿井，斗而铸锥，不亦晚乎！

Compliance with the law of yin and yang means life; failing to comply with it means death.

Those who fail to comply with the law of yin and yang would be setting their bodies against nature.

No, thanks!

The complier would enjoy safety and peace; the failure would suffer chaos and disaster.

That is just like governing a state; don't just try to suppress a revolt only when it has broken out .

What have you done?

I've just sent the baby for an inoculation.

Therefore the wise emphasize prevention rather than cure of illnesses.

I want to dig a well to quench my thirst.

The enemy has penetrated into the city! I have to sharpen my spear.

Treatise on the Interaction of Life Qi with Heaven

The yang qi in the body and nature's yang qi are closely related. Harmony between the two, and a balance of the yin and yang in the body, are essential for good health.

原文：黄帝曰：夫自古通天者，生之本，本于阴阳。天地之间，六合之内，其气九州，九窍、五脏、十二节，皆通乎天气。其生五，其气三。数犯此者，则邪气伤人，此寿命之本也。

It has been recognized since ancient times that life is closely connected with nature, and the foundation of life lies in yin and yang.

All things in the universe— whether the land or ...

... the nine orifices of the body, the five viscera and the twelve joints - are interactive with the heaven qi.

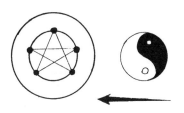

The heaven's yin and yang give rise to the earth's five elements, which in turn interact with heaven's three yin and three yang.

Those who act against this mutual interaction between heaven, earth and man would be injured by noxious influences. One's health and life depend on his compliance with the law of yin and yang.

原文：阳气者，若天与日，失其所，则折寿而不彰。故天运当以日光明，是故阳因而上，卫外者也。

The yang qi in one's body is similar to the sun. If movement of the sun becomes abnormal, no living things can survive.

If movement of the yang qi in one's body becomes irregular, one will suffer a premature death.

Heavenly bodies owe their regular, perpetual movements to the strong influence of the sun.

Like the strong influence of the sun, the yang qi in one's body is to rise and expand outwards to protect one's body.

原文：因于寒，欲如运枢，起居如惊，神气乃浮。因于暑、汗、烦则喘喝，静则多言，体若燔炭，汗出而散。因于湿，首如裹；篇热不攘，大筋缑短，小筋弛长，缑短为拘，弛长为痿。因于气，为肿，四维相代，阳气乃竭。

When it is cold, one should stay indoors and preserve one's yang qi by acting like the door axle, turning about its pivot as the door opens and closes.

You're drunk ...

If one lives an undisciplined life, circulation of yang qi will be disturbed and it will be gradually depleted.

If injured by the summer heat, one will perspire profusely and, if agitated, pant noisily.

If injured by damp, one will feel heavy in the head as if it has been bandaged. Prolonged exposure will result in muscle cramps and general weakness.

If the heat penetrates deeply and injures the yang qi, then even if not agitated, one will become loquacious. The body will become hot like burning charcoal and the heat can be dispersed only through perspiration.

Swollen!

The weakness of yang qi will result in swelling limbs, which in turn will exhaust the yang qi.

原文：阳气者，烦劳则张，精绝；辟积于夏，使人煎厥。目盲不可以视，耳闭不可以听，溃溃乎若坏都，汩汩乎不可止。阳气者，大怒则形气绝，而血菀于上，使人薄厥。

If the condition persists and is aggravated by summer heat, the disease of *bailing reversal will result.

When one is weary as a result of overwork, the yang qi in the body will overflourish, causing a relative depletion of the yin essence.

The onslaught of the disease is so severe that it is as turbulent as a river that has breached the dikes.

The body's yang qi can also be thrown into chaos with great anger. The resultant blockage of channels and collaterals and the stagnation of blood in the upper part will cause dizziness or even faintness.

Among the main symptoms is rapid deterioration of sight and hearing.

*condition where the imbalances in the yin-yang qi results in the loss of consciousness.

原文：有伤于筋，纵，其若不容，汗出偏沮，使人偏枯。汗出见湿，乃生痤疿。高粱之变，足生大丁，受如持虚。劳汗当风，寒薄为皶，郁乃痤。

When the sinews are injured, they become flabby and cannot be controlled at will.

Oh ...

Perspiration on only one half of the body may lead to partial paralysis.

湿邪
Noxious damp

Invasion by noxious damp after perspiration will result in prickly heat and acne.

27

Those who indulge in eating rich food are prone to having sores.

They are as easily afflicted by disease as an empty vessel would be filled with things.

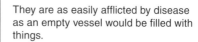

Brothers, our target has appeared. Who will go?

I will!

Pathogens

All of us!

If after working and perspiring one's skin is invaded by cold air, pimples will result.

Cold air

If the condition persists, acne will result.

Oh! How awful!

原文：阳气者，精则养神，柔则养筋。开阖不得，寒气从之，乃生大偻；陷脉为瘘；留连肉腠，俞气化薄；传为善畏，及为惊骇；营气不从，逆于肉理，乃生痈肿；魄汗未尽，形弱而气烁，穴俞以闭，发为风疟。

The essence of yang qi nourishes the spirit, its gentleness nourishes the muscles.

Oh ... I've been injured by cold!

If the opening and closing of the pores are out of control, cold will sneak into the body doing harm to its yang qi. Cold stagnating in the muscles will result in difficulty in bending and straightening the body.

Cold stagnating in the blood vessels will result in fistula and other forms of ulcers.

Ouch!

Invasion of the viscera by cold via the acupuncture points will result in the condition of being easily frightened.

Ghost!

If the invading cold affects the smooth circulation of nourishing qi and stagnates in the muscles, swellings and sores will result.

When a perspiring and tired person is suddenly exposed to cold wind, the perspiration stagnating between the skin and muscles will block the acupuncture points and result in a cold.

ACHOOO!

I've caught a cold!

原文：故风者，百病之始也。清静则肉腠闭拒，虽有大风苛毒，弗之能害。此因时之序也。

Evil wind is the cause of many diseases.

When the mind is free of cravings and the body is not weary, the skin and flesh are well protected by yang qi. Then, even a strong evil wind cannot harm the body.

The key to this is living in accord with seasonal changes of nature.

原文：故病久则转化，上下不并，良医弗为。故阳畜积病死，而阳气当隔，隔者当写，不亟正治，粗乃败之。故阳气者，一日而主外，平旦人气生；日中而阳气隆；日西而阳气已虚，气门乃闭。是故暮而收拒，无拢筋骨，无见雾露。反此三时，形乃困薄。

If a sickness lasts for a long time, there is a danger that it might spread. When it reaches the state where the upper and lower parts of the body cannot communicate, even a good physician won't be able to help.

Why didn't he seek treatment earlier?

An excessive accumulation of yang qi can be fatal too. When a blockage results from such an accumulation, it has to be purged.

Lead Croton (a purgative) and other generals to open up the pass at once.

Yes!

If not treated promptly and if the patient has an incompetent physician, his life will be in danger.

He needs strong tonics.

31

THE BODY CAMP

During the day, yang qi in the body mainly protects the surface area against disease. At dawn, it begins to be active on the skin.

As the sun moves westward, yang qi declines gradually and the pores close up.

Rest at night to allow yang qi to decline and the pores to remain closed. Do not exert yourself or expose yourself to mist and dew.

It is most abundant at midday.

Violating the rhythm of the operating yang qi will result in the body being invaded by evil qi.

Charge!

Charge!

原文：岐伯曰：阴者，藏精而起亟也；阳者，卫外而为固也。阴不皮其阳，则脉流薄疾，并乃狂；阳不皮其阴，则五藏气争，九窍不通。是以圣人陈阴阳，筋脉和同，骨髓坚固，气血皆从；如是则内外调和，邪不能害，耳目聪明，气立如故。

Qibo said: Yin stores vital energy and is the source of qi in the body; yang protects the exterior of the body and at the same time guards against the dissipation of yin through leakage.

In the *five elements, the horse has a yang character.

It's galloping off without me!

Yin and yang are mutually restraining. If yin cannot restrain yang, it will result in a quick strong pulse.

One could go mad if yang qi in the body becomes too strong.

*Refer to page 41

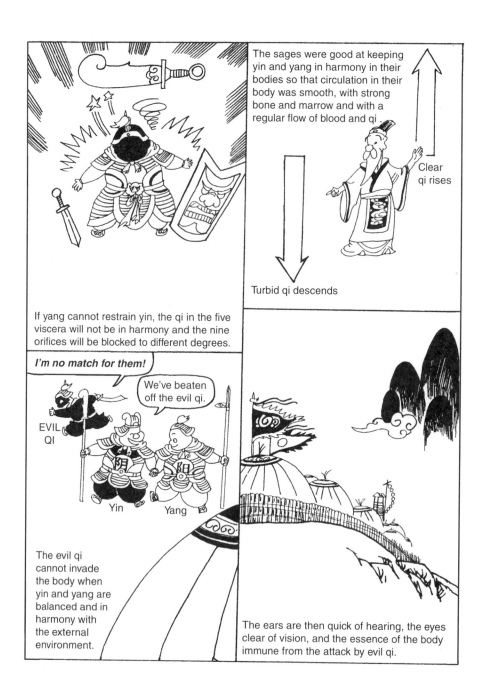

The sages were good at keeping yin and yang in harmony in their bodies so that circulation in their body was smooth, with strong bone and marrow and with a regular flow of blood and qi.

Clear qi rises

Turbid qi descends

If yang cannot restrain yin, the qi in the five viscera will not be in harmony and the nine orifices will be blocked to different degrees.

I'm no match for them!

We've beaten off the evil qi.

EVIL QI

Yin

Yang

The evil qi cannot invade the body when yin and yang are balanced and in harmony with the external environment.

The ears are then quick of hearing, the eyes clear of vision, and the essence of the body immune from the attack by evil qi.

原文：风客淫气，精乃亡，邪伤肝也。因而饱食，筋脉横解，肠澼为痔；因而大饮，则气逆；因而强力，肾气乃伤，高骨乃坏。

Over-eating will result in rupture of blood vessels in the stomach and intestines.

This will lead to dysentery or bleeding piles.

Over-drinking will cause an upsurge of lung qi and hiccuping.

Over-exerting physically will cause dizziness.

All these can injure the kidneys and the spinal column.

原文：凡阴阳之要，阳密乃固。两者不和，若
春无秋，若冬无夏；因而和之，是谓圣度。故
阳强不能密，阴气乃绝；阴平阳密，精神乃治
；阴阳离决，精气乃绝。

The general principle of yin-yang harmony is that yang qi should be kept strong and dense so that yin qi can remain placid and gentle.

If yin and yang are not in harmony,
it will be like spring without autumn
and winter without summer.

Therefore, maintenance of harmony of yin and yang is the best principle for maintaining good health.

If yang qi is over flourishing without being solid and dense, yin qi will decline.

Yin

Charge!

AAH!

One's spirit can only be in perfect order when yin qi is placid and yang qi solid and dense.

Yin qi

Vital energy

Yang qi

If yin and yang part their ways, the vital energy will be destroyed.

原文：阴之所生，本在五味；阴之五官，伤在五味。是故味过于酸，肝气以津，脾气乃绝，味过于咸，大骨气劳，短肌，心气抑；味过于甘，心气喘满，色黑，肾气不衡；味过于苦，脾气不濡，胃气乃厚；味过于辛，筋脉沮弛，精神乃央。是故谨和五味，骨正筋柔，气血以流，腠理以密，如是则骨气以精。谨道如法，长有天命。

The yin vital energy originates in the five flavours. But the five zang viscera that store vital energy can be injured by excessive intake of the five flavours.

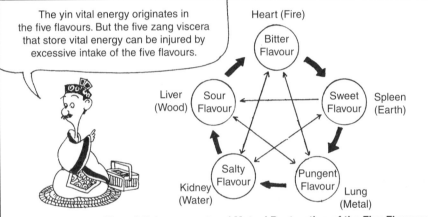

Heart (Fire)

Bitter Flavour

Liver (Wood) — Sour Flavour

Sweet Flavour — Spleen (Earth)

Salty Flavour

Pungent Flavour

Kidney (Water)

Lung (Metal)

Mutual Enhancement and Mutual Destruction of the Five Flavours

Eating too much sour food will cause the liver to produce excessive liver qi which injures the spleen qi.

That'll produce excessive internal heat.

Eating too much salty food will injure the large bones, emaciate the muscles and flesh and cause depression.

Oh my legs!

You've taken too much salt!

39

Eating too much sweet food will cause depression, darkness on the face and unbalanced kidney qi.

Take a look in the mirror.

My face is so dark.

Eating too much bitter food will deprive the nourishment of the spleen, causing indigestion and distention in the stomach.

ERRH!

ERRH!

Eating too much pungent food will cause the muscles and pulse to become slack and injure the spirit.

Wow, it's really hot!

If people regulate their intake of the five flavours, their bones will remain straight and solid, their muscles will remain pliable, their qi and blood will circulate well, the interstices will be compact, and consequently, their bone qi will be strong. If they strictly observe this principle of maintaining good health, they will enjoy longevity endowed by nature.

Treatise on the Truth of the Golden Coffer

The Truth of the Golden Coffer is a scientific document kept by ancient rulers. According to the Five Element Theory, the year is divided into the five seasons of spring, summer, autumn, winter and the long summer. These seasons are closely related with the five zang viscera, and seasonal changes are manifested in the relevant organs.

原文：所谓得四时胜者：春胜长夏，长夏胜冬，冬胜夏，夏胜秋，秋胜春，所谓四时之胜也。

The ancients categorized complex relationships in the universe into either mutually enhancing or mutually restraining. They also designated metal, wood, water, fire and earth as the five elements to illustrate these relationships more vividly.

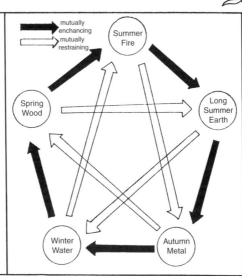

The body will only be healthy if it functions in conformity to the proper interactions of the five elements. Any disruption in these interactions will result in illness. Spring is warm: liver qi starts to grow. Summer is hot: heart qi starts to grow. Autumn is dry: lung qi wanes. Winter is cold: kidney qi is concealed.

The ancients matched the seasons with the five elements i.e. spring with wood, summer with fire, long summer with earth, autumn with metal and winter with water so as to illustrate the influence of the seasons on the five zang viscera.

1st and 2nd lunar months: the body qi resides in the liver.
3rd and 4th lunar months: the body qi resides in the spleen.
5th and 6th lunar months: the body qi resides in the head.
7th and 8th lunar months: the body qi resides in the lungs.
9th and 10th lunar months: the body qi resides in the heart.
11th and 12th lunar months: the body qi resides in the kidneys.

The Great Treatise on the Interaction of Yin And Yang

Yin and yang are opposite yet unified and interdependent. Changes in yin, yang and the five elements in nature are closely linked with changes in the body's five viscera.

Ouch! Cramps again!

Too much wind can cause cramps and trembling of the limbs.

Too much heat can cause swellings.

Yes, red and swollen.

Too much dryness can cause a depletion of body fluids and relevant illness.

This is no obesity; it's dropsy.

Too much cold can cause dropsy (swelling due to an abnormal accumulation of watery fluid in any part of the body).

It's terrible!

Too much damp can cause diarrhoea.

原文：天有四时五行，以生长收藏，以生寒暑燥湿风。人有五脏化五气，以生喜怒悲忧恐。故喜怒伤气，寒暑伤形，暴怒伤阴，暴喜伤阳。……喜怒不节，寒暑过度，生乃不固。故重阴必阳，重阳必阴。

Seasonal changes and interactions of the five elements give rise to climatic changes of cold, heat, dryness, damp and wind. They affect all things in nature and shape the laws of birth, growth, transformation, harvest and storage.

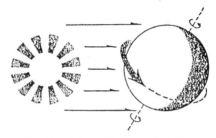

Earth's rotation with day and night

Man has five zang viscera: the liver, heart, spleen, lung and kidney. The qi in them gives rise to the emotions of joy, anger, sorrow, worry and fear.

43

原文：故曰：天地者，万物之上下也；阴阳者，血气之男女也；左右者，阴阳之道路也；水火者，阴阳之征兆也；阴阳者，万物之能始也。故曰：阴在内，阳在外，阴之使也。

Heaven is at the top and earth is at the bottom, and all things in creation exist in between them. Yin and yang, like blood and qi or men and women, are mutually interacting.

Water, which is cold in character, and fire, which is hot in character, are the symbols of yin and yang.

Hence, yin and yang are mutually interacting.

Yin, active within, is protected by yang; yang, active outside, is motivated by yin.

原文：帝曰：调此二者奈何？岐伯曰：能知七损八益，则二者可调，不知用此，则早衰之节也……愚者不足，智者有余；有余则耳目聪明，身体轻强，老者复壮，壮者益治。是以圣人为无为之事，乐恬憺之能，以欲快志于虚无之守，故寿命无穷，与天地终。

The Yellow Emperor: How shall we harmonize yin and yang so that neither is excessive or deficient?

The rhythm of a woman's life is based on every seven years, and it is desirable that she has a regular menstrual discharge. The rhythm of a man's life is based on every eight years, and it is desirable that he has his reproductive qi in abundance.

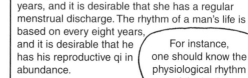

For instance, one should know the physiological rhythm of the body.

What are they?

Qibo: First, you must know the "sevenfold reduction" and "eightfold boost", two principles of maintaining good health.

That old man!

The gist of the principles of "sevenfold reduction" and "eightfold boost" is to regulate the flow of vital energy and build up the blood qi. When the vital energy is full, yin and yang will be in harmony.

Why am I still not home?

One who does not know how to maintain good health often feels inadequate in energy.

You are not fit.

One who knows how to maintain good health often finds himself having surplus energy.

You are in tip-top condition, Grandpa.

One with surplus energy has sharp ears and good eyesight, is agile, and enjoys robust health even in old age.

This is the way to maintain good health.

Therefore the wise do not exert themselves or think wildly. They are always optimistic, cheerful and tranquil, and are able to live to a ripe old age.

原文：故清阳为天，浊阴为地。地气上为云，天气下为雨；雨出地气，云出天气。故清阳出上窍，浊阴出下窍；清阳发腠理，浊阴走五脏；清阳实四支，浊阴归六腑。

Wow, I feel great!

Likewise in the body, the clear yang qi exits by the upper orifices.

In nature, the clear yang qi rises to become the heaven and the turbid yin qi descends to become the earth. The earth qi vaporizes and rises to form clouds; the heaven qi condenses and falls as rain.

The turbid yin qi exits by the lower orifices.

The clear yang qi emanates from within and resides in the interstices and the limbs; the turbid yin qi flows inwards and circulates in the five zang viscera and six fu organs.

The Yellow Emperor: What is the Reason?

原文：帝曰：何以然？岐伯曰：东方阳也，阳者其精并于上，并于上，则上明而下虚，故使耳目聪明，而手足不便也；西方阴也，阴者其精并于下，并于下，则下盛而上虚，故其耳目不聪明，而手足便也。故俱感于邪，其在上则右甚，在下则左甚，此天地阴阳所不能全也，故邪居之。

Qibo: The east is associated with yang, which has the tendency to rise. So the body's vital energy tends to concentrate in the upper part, giving good hearing and clear vision but bringing no advantage to the hands and feet.

The west is associated with yin, which has the tendency to descend. So the body's vital energy tends to concentrate in the lower part, impairing hearing and vision but invigorating the hands and the feet.

When the left and the right sides have been simultaneously hit by noxious wind ...

Oh, I've been hit by noxious wind.

In the upper part of the body, the right side will be more seriously affected; and in the lower part, the left side will be more seriously affected.

Charge! charge! charge!

風邪 Evil wind

Just as imbalance of yin and yang exists between heaven and earth, there are also imbalances of yin and yang between the left and right sides of the body. Evil qi can take advantage of such imbalances to invade and stay in the body.

50

原文：味厚者为阴，薄为阴之阳；气厚者为阳，薄为阳之阴。味厚则泄，薄则通；气薄则发泄，厚则发热。壮火之气衰，少火之气壮，壮火食气，气食少火，壮火散气，少火生气。气味辛甘发散为阳，酸苦涌泄为阴。

A rich flavour has a pure yin character, of which a thinner flavour is considered yang within yin. A strong smell has a pure yang character, of which a faint smell is considered yin within yang.

Where's the loo?

That with a flavour too rich can cause diarrhoea. When the yang fire becomes too strong, the true essence qi will be exhausted.

The pungent and sweet flavours with a dispersing effect have a yang character. The sour and bitter flavours with a purging effect have a yin character.

Yang qi, when it gets too strong, can hurt the original qi. But the original qi is dependent on normal yang qi. It is therefore important to maintain an appropriate level of yang qi.

That with a faint smell can clear the passages of the channels and their collaterals. Normal yang qi can strengthen the true essence qi.

原文：阴胜则阳病，阳胜则阴病。阳胜则热，阴胜则寒。重寒则热，重热则寒。寒伤形热伤气；气伤痛，形伤肿。故先痛而后肿者，气伤形也；先肿而后痛者，形伤气也。

Yin and yang in the body are in a state of kinetic balance. If yin qi triumphs over yang qi, the latter will be hurt, and vice versa.

The effects of yang qi overwhelming yin qi are manifested as heat, and at its extreme state, heat will turn into cold.

Heat can injure the body's qi resulting in pain.

Ouch!

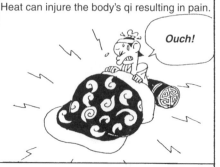

Cold can injure the body, resulting in swellings.

It's swollen.

So, if pain comes before swelling, it is the result of qi being injured before the body is injured; if swelling comes before pain, it is the result of the body being hurt before qi.

原文：天不足西北，故西北方阴也，而人右耳目不如左明也；地不满东南，故东南方阳也，而人左手足不如右强也。

The northwest, which is deficient in heaven qi, has a yin character. Man's hearing and eyesight on the right side are not as sharp as those on the left side.

The northwest, with many high mountains, is relatively cold. It is yin in character and deficient in heaven qi.

The southeast, with a yang character, is relatively hot. It faces the sea, so people say that the earth is incomplete in the southeast.

The southeast, deficient in earth qi, is yang in character. Man's hands and legs on the left side are not as strong as those on the right side.

53

原文：以天地为之阴阳，阳之汗，以天地之雨名之；阳之气，以天地之疾风名之。暴气象雷；逆气象阳。故治不法天之纪，不用地之理，则灾害至矣！

Yin and yang in the body are similar to those in nature. Perspiration, the result of the discharge of yang qi, is like rain from the heaven.

HA HA, I've become an immortal!

The body's yang qi is like strong winds.

One who does not follow nature's laws in caring for one's health will fall ill.

The qi of man's violent rage is like thunder.

The upward, counter-flowing qi is like the sun's fire.

Treatise on Differentiating Between Yin and Yang

The body's channels and viscera are intimately linked with nature's yin and yang. For instance, the heart and liver are yang organs while the lung, spleen and kidney are yin organs. Being able to distinguish between the yin and yang properties of diseases is important for their understanding.

原文：黄帝问曰：人有四经十二从，何谓？岐伯对曰：四经应四时，十二从应十二月，十二月应十二脉……别于阳者，知病忌时；别于阴者，知死生之期。谨熟阴阳，无与众谋。

The body has four pulse conditions, namely, those of the liver, heart, lung and kidney, that correspond respectively to the four seasons of spring, summer, autumn and winter.

Identification of the yang stomach pulse enables one to know the dos and don'ts of various seasons and diseases.

Mutton is yang in character and a winter food item. Eating it in summer will give rise to pathogenic fire.

Identification of the true pulse of the viscera of yin character enables one to predict the time of death of a patient.

A good understanding of the yin and yang pulses will dispel any doubts and uncertainties.

原文：
岐伯曰：二阳之病发
心脾，有不得隐曲，
女子不月。其传为风
消，其传为息贲者，
死不治。

Generally speaking, disease of the digestive system affects the heart and spleen and causes embarrassing conditions.

Oh, how am I going to tell?

In a woman, it causes irregular menstruation or even menstrual block.

Why has it stopped flowing?

In time, the dissipating wind-wasting thirst develops. The patient becomes feverish and loses weight as the body fluids dry up slowly.

The patient may also deteriorate into rapid respiration characterized by panting, which will be difficult to cure.

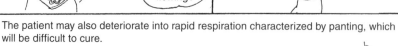

Poor Dad!

原文：
三阳为病，发寒热，下为痈肿，及为痿厥腨㾓。其传为索泽，其传为颓疝。

The third yang, or the greater yang, reflects the channels of the small intestines and bladder. Diseases of the greater yang channels are generally characterized by chill and fever ...

... or swelling of the lower limbs ...

... or general weakness of the feet.

... or swelling of the scrotum.

If allowed to persist, the condition may result in dry, scaly skin ...

原文：
一阳发病，少气，善咳，善泄。其传为心掣。其传为隔。

The first yang, or the lesser yang, refers to the channels of the triple burner and gallbladder. Diseases of the lesser yang channels are generally characterized by general weakness and shortness of breath.

The patient is prone to coughing ...

COUGH!
COUGH!

... or diarrhoea.

If allowed to persist, the condition may result in heart vacuity manifested as palpitation ...

... or constipation.

原文：二阳一阴发病，主惊骇，背痛，善噫，善欠，名曰风厥。二阴一阳发病，善胀，心满善气。三阳三阴发病，为偏枯痿易，四支不举。

The first yin or the reverting yin, refers to the channels of the liver and pericardium. Diseases of yang brightness and the reversing yin are characterized by terror, backaches and belching.

The second yin, or the lesser yin, refers to the channels of the heart and kidneys. Diseases of the lesser yin and lesser yang are characterized by distention of the abdomen, chest congestion and sighing.

Oh, this is terrible!

The third yin, or the greater yin, refers to the channels of the lung and spleen. Diseases of the greater yang and greater yin will lead to paralysis on one side of the body ...

... or weakness of the muscles ...

I can't even lift my arms.

... or the condition that the four limbs cannot be raised or moved.

Treatise on Different Methods of Treatment and Appropriate Prescriptions

People living in different regions have different constitutions and are affected by different diseases. Physicians ought to use appropriate methods of treatment for different patients in different regions.

原文：故东方之域，天地之所始生也，鱼盐之地，海滨傍水。其民食鱼而嗜咸，皆安其处，美其食。鱼者使人热中，盐者胜血，故其民皆黑色疏理，其病皆为痈疡，其治宜砭石。故砭石者，亦从东方来。

The eastern region, blessed with a mild, conducive climate, produces plenty of fish and salt.

Because of their proximity to the sea, the people there eat a great deal of fish and like salty food.

They live happily.

These fish are delicious!

Splendid!

However, excessive consumption of fish, which have a fiery character, generates too much internal heat.

Excessive intake of salt hurts the blood. Therefore, most Easterners have a dark complexion and loose muscles.

It's the same as what I had previously.

So the method of treatment with a stone needle originates from the East.

They are often afflicted by sores. The usual method of treatment is to drain the sore by puncturing it with a stone needle.

原文：西方者，金玉之域，沙石之处，天地之所收引也。其民陵居而多风，水土刚强，其民不衣而以褐荐，其民华食而脂肥，故邪不能伤其形体，其病生于内，其治宜毒药。故毒药者，亦从西方来。

The western region, comprising mostly mountains and deserts, is rich in precious metals and gemstones. Its natural environment has the restraining characteristics of the autumn season.

A gem stone!

They live a simple life, wearing animal skins and sleeping on straw mats.

The people here live in spartan, windy dwellings on hill slopes. The rugged living conditions make them a tough lot.

 原文：北方者，天地所闭藏之域也，其地高陵居，风寒冰冽。其民乐野处而乳食，藏寒生满病，其治宜灸焫。故灸焫者，亦从北方来。

By the Chile River, below the Yinshan Mountains, the sky is like a tent covering the land. Vast is the sky, boundless the wilds. Sheep and cattle are grazing on the wind-swept meadow ...

The northern region, comprising mostly highlands, has the same storing characteristics as the winter season.

The people often have to contend with bitter cold winds, frost and ice.

They are happy with their nomadic life,
staying in tents and living on milk products.

Thus their viscera are susceptible to chills
and they often suffer from abdominal
distention. These diseases are best treated
with cauterization by burning moxa.

原文：南方者，天地所长养，阳之所盛处也，其地下，水土弱，雾露之所聚也。其民嗜酸而食腑，故其民皆致理而赤色，其病挛痹，其治宜微针。故九针者，亦从南方来。

The South, with a hot climate and the greatest abundance of yang qi, is a region of growth and nourishment. Its low-lying land collects dew and mist.

The people here prefer sour food and fermented soybean products!

66

67

原文：中央者，其地平以湿，天地所以生万物也众。其民食杂而不劳，故其病多痿厥寒热，其治宜导引按跷。故导引按跷者，亦从中央出也。故圣人杂合以治，各得其所宜。故治所以异而病皆愈者，得病之情，知治之大体也。

The central region is level and moist. It is a land of many produces.

A great variety of food is available and the people live a relatively easy and comfortable life.

I think the fourth girl of the Wangs is a pretty good choice.

Our son ought to marry in a few years.

Common diseases here are:

weak limbs

reverse flow

chills and fever

These diseases are best treated with conduction and massage. Thus, the method of treatment with conduction and massage has its origin in the central region.

Conduction and Massage Treatment

Is it here?

Ouch! Precisely!

A competent physician should master all these methods of treatment and apply the most suitable therapy according to the specific case.

Treatise on the Subtle Skill of Pulse Examination

Variations in a person's pulse condition are complex. Accurate diagnosis by taking a patient's pulse is of vital importance to the treatment of his illness. By using the four diagnostic techniques of observing, listening, questioning and palpating, it is possible to ascertain roughly the patient's condition.

原文：五藏者，中之守也。中盛藏满，气胜伤恐者，声如从室中言，是中气之湿也；言而微，终日乃复言者，此夺气也；衣被不敛，言语善恶不避亲疏者，此神明之乱也；仓廪不藏者，是门户不要也；水泉不止者，是膀胱不藏也。得守者生，失守者死。

The five zang viscera are where the body's vitality is stored and guarded.

A distended abdomen and a deep, raucous voice like sounds emitting from an enclosed room would indicate damp in the middle burner repressing the centre qi.

A faint voice and difficulty in uttering a complete sentence indicate insufficiency in the centre qi.

Disorderly movements of the limbs, incoherent speech and inability to recognize relatives would indicate emotional disturbance (disturbed heart spirit).

Inability of the stomach and intestines to hold water and grain with incessant diarrhoea would indicate dysfunction of the spleen and stomach.

Treatise on Regulation of Visceral Qi by the Seasons

Physiological functions and changes in diseases of the five viscera are regulated by the seasons and interactions of the Five Elements. The gravity of diseases of the viscera, and even life and death, connected with these.

原文：病在肝，愈于夏；夏不愈，甚于秋；秋不死，持至冬，起于春，禁当风。……肝病者，平旦慧，下晡甚，夜半静。肝欲散，急食辛以散之，用辛补之，酸写之。

Disease of the liver is cured more easily in summer. The patient usually feels better at dawn.

If not cured in summer, the disease would worsen in autumn. The condition is worst at sunset but eases off in the later half of the night.

It hurts terribly at this hour each day.

If the patient survives, his condition will remain relatively stable in winter.

How do you feel now?

Fine. But it still hurts at times.

Pungent medicines are needed promptly to disperse qi from the liver.

The patient's condition can only improve the following spring. Exposure to wind should be avoided.

Use pungent medicines as tonics for the liver and sour medicines to purge the liver.

原文：病在心，愈在长夏；长夏不愈，甚写于冬；冬不死，持于春，起于夏，禁温食热衣……心病者，日中慧，夜半甚，平旦静。心欲耎，急食咸以耎之，用咸补之，甘写之。

Disease of the heart can be cured more easily in long summer (the sixth lunar month). The patient usually feels better at noon.

If not cured in the long summer, it would become graver in winter. The condition is worst at midnight but eases off at dawn.

Another attack? How bad is it?

If the patient survives, his condition will remain stable in the following spring.

Better now?

Not bad.

Disease of the heart requires a softening cure. Salty medicines are needed promptly for that effect. Use the same medicines as tonics for the heart.

Condition of the patient can only improve in summer. Avoid food of a heaty nature and avoid wearing too many clothes. Sweet medicines are needed to purge the heart.

原文：病在脾，愈在秋；秋不愈，甚于春；春不死，持于夏，起于长夏，禁温食饱食、湿地濡衣。……脾病者，日昳慧出甚，下晡静。脾欲缓，急食甘以缓之，用苦写之，甘补之。

Diseases of the spleen can be cured more easily in autumn. The patient feels better in the afternoon.

I feel better only at this time.

It begins to ache at dawn everyday.

Cock-a-doodle-doo..

If not cured in autumn, the case will be aggravated in spring. The condition is worst at sunrise but eases at sunset.

I am feeling much better now.

If the patient survives the spring, his condition will remain stable in summer but will not get better until the long summer. Sweet medicines are to be used as a moderator for the disease.

Avoid overeating or taking food of a heaty nature. Do not wear wet clothes or live near wet places.

Yes, just eat to be 70% full. I won't eat any more.

If necessary, use bitter medicines for draining, or use sweet medicines as a tonic.

原文：病在肺，愈在冬；冬不愈，甚于夏；夏不死，持于长夏，起于秋，禁寒饮食寒衣……肺病者，下晡慧，日中甚，夜半静。肺欲收，急食酸以收之，用酸补之，辛写之。

Diseases of the lungs can be cured more easily in winter. The patient feels better towards dusk.

If not cured in winter, the case will be aggravated in summer. The condition is the worst at noon, but eases off in the afternoon.

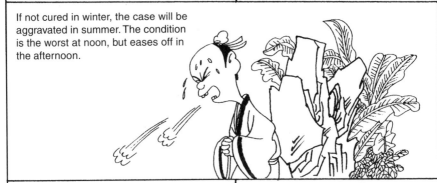

If the patient survives the summer, his condition will remain stable during long summer, but will not get better until autumn.

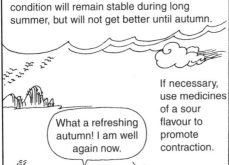

What a refreshing autumn! I am well again now.

If necessary, use medicines of a sour flavour to promote contraction.

Wear warm clothes and avoid eating cold food.

If necessary, use sour medicine as a tonic, or use pungent medicine for draining.

75

原文：病在肾，愈在春；春不愈，甚于长夏；长夏不死，持于秋，起于冬，禁犯焠焫热食温炙衣……肾病者，夜半慧，四季甚，下晡静。肾欲坚，急食苦以坚之，用苦补之，咸写之。

Diseases of the kidneys are cured more easily in spring. The patient feels better around midnight.

This is the only time of the day when he is a bit better.

If not cured in spring, the case will be aggravated during long summer. The condition is more serious during 7 to 9 a.m. & p.m. and 1 to 3 a.m. & p.m., but eases off at dusk.

Still ill?

I didn't expect it to be more serious now.

If the patient survives the long summer, his condition will remain stable in autumn, but will not get better until winter. If necessary, use bitter medicine for solidification.

I do recover in such cold weather.

Avoid eating heaty food or wearing clothes straight from fire drying. If necessary, use bitter medicine as a supplement or salty medicine to drain the kidneys.

76

原文：毒药攻邪，五谷为养，五果为助，五畜为益，五菜为充，气味而服之，以补精益气。此五者，有辛、酸、甘、苦、咸，各有所利，或散、或收、或缓、或急、或坚、或耎，四时五藏，病随五味所宜也。

Poisons are used to attack the evil.

Grains and cereals are for nourishment.

Fruits serve as their adjuvants.

Vegetables are consumed for additional nourishment.

Various kinds of animal meat are for supplement.

What a rich variety of food!

Consumption of a harmonious combination of various flavours of food can supplement the vital energy.

The above mentioned things have different flavours: pungent, sour, sweet, bitter, or salty. Each flavour benefits the qi of a particular zang organ.

Treatise on the Qi of the Five Zang Viscera

Each of the five zang viscera has its aversion and engenders a particular humour. And there are five overstrains which injure the qi of the five viscera.

原文：五脏所恶；心恶热，肺恶寒，肝恶风，脾恶湿，肾恶燥。是谓五恶。

The heart is averse to heat, as it is susceptible to diseases caused by heat that injures the yin blood.

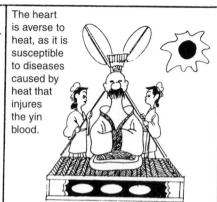

The lungs are averse to cold, as they are susceptible to diseases caused by cold that affects the lung qi from being diffused.

The liver is averse to wind which it tends to produce, and too much wind will give rise to hypertonicity.

The spleen is averse to damp, as it is susceptible to diseases caused by damp and excessive damp may give rise to swelling abscesses.

The kidneys are averse to dryness, as the kidney yin is susceptible to depletion and excessive dryness will desiccate the yin essence.

Each of the Five Zang Viscera Engenders a Humour

79

Treatise on the Preservation of Health

Everyone on earth have the desire to preserve their health and enjoy a long life. Since life is closely related with nature, man should accommodate and adapt to the natural laws. The principles of the five elements will help people to have a better understanding of the ways to preserve health.

原文：黄帝问曰：天覆地载，万物悉备，莫贵于人。人以天地之气生，四时之法成，君王众庶，尽欲全形，形之疾病，莫知其情，留淫日深，著于骨髓，心私虑之。余欲针除其疾病，为之奈何？岐伯对曰：夫盐之味咸者，其气令器津泄，弦绝者，其音嘶败；木敷者，其叶发；病深者，其声哕。人有此三者，是为坏府，毒药无治，短针无取，此皆绝皮伤肉，血气争黑。

Of all the things on the earth, nothing is more precious than human beings. People live on the qi of heaven and earth and the essence of water and food, and grow with the laws of the seasons.

Everyone, from the monarch to the common citizens, have the desire to preserve their health.

Darling, you don't look well.

I'm ill.

Qibo: Salt stored in a container gradually seeps a fluid. That is the draining of the qi of salt.

But very often an illness begins when one is unaware of it. Thus the disease progresses deep into the bones and marrow. What is the way to alleviate people's sufferings?

On the verge of breaking, a string on a musical instrument will make a brittle sound.

A tree without strong roots will wither despite the apparent luxuriance of its twigs and leaves.

When the disease gets serious, the patient will feel like vomiting.

Why? Your voice sounds strange.

I'm not feeling well these days.

That is the manifestation of serious injury to the internal organs and dissipation of the blood and qi, and it will be difficult to get cured with medicine, acupuncture and moxibustion.

原文：帝曰：人生有形，不离阴阳，天地合气，别为九野，分为四时，月有大小，日有短长，万物并至，不可胜量，虚实呿吟，敢问其方？岐伯曰：木得金而伐，火得水而灭，土得木而达，金得火而缺，水得土而绝。万物尽然，不可胜竭。

The Yellow Emperor: There are countless changes between vacuity and repletion within the human body. What is the way to understand and treat these changes?

Qibo: The principles of relations of the five elements can be followed in this respect. For instance, metal can cut wood.

Water can put out fire.

Wood can penetrate earth.

Fire can melt metal.

Earth can hold water.

Treatise on the Nature of Vacuity and Repletion

Vacuity and repletion refer to the state of pathogen and antipathogen qi. Vacuity is a state where the antipathogen qi is insufficient, and repletion a state where the pathogen is abundant.

原文：凡治消瘅、仆击、偏枯、痿厥、气满发逆，肥贵人则高粱之疾也。隔塞，闭绝，上下不通，则暴忧之病也。暴厥而聋，偏塞闭不通，内气暴薄也。不从内，外中风之病，故瘦留著也。跖跛，寒风湿之病也。

To treat pure heat-wasting thirst, sudden syncope, hemilateral withering, wilting reversal, panting counterflow, etc., it is necessary to discriminate between different cases.

For obese patients, the diseases are generally caused by indulgence in rich food.

Chest and epigastric fullness and obstruction condition are caused by rage or psychological trauma.

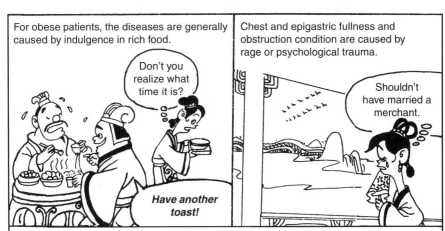

Sudden reverse flow, loss of consciousness or hearing, and obstruction of bowel or urine are generally induced by the sudden chaos of qi.

Some diseases are induced by the invasion of exogenous wind evil that may linger between muscles, tendons and bones, engendering heat, and consuming flesh and muscles. Among other manifestations is difficulty in walking caused by the invasion of wind, cold or damp.

Treatise on Differentiation of Pains

All diseases are caused by malfunction of the qi. Rage makes qi ascend; joyousness makes the qi flow and disperse freely; grief makes the qi diminish; fright makes the qi descend; chill makes the qi contract; heat makes the qi escape; being startled makes the qi scatter and become chaotic; overstraining depletes the qi; and excessive thought and obsession make the qi stagnant.

原文：余知百病生于气也，怒则气上，喜则气缓，悲则气消，恐则气下，寒则气收，炅则气泄，惊则气乱，劳则气耗，思则气结。

Qibo: Rage makes the qi ascend and in serious cases may cause vomiting of blood or dysentery.

Joy will soothe the flow of qi and make it disperse freely, enabling the nourishing qi and defence qi to permeate throughout the body.

Sadness and grief cause the lungs to overexpand, so that the upper burner will be stagnated, the nourishing and defence qi will not disperse, and heat will be accumulated in the chest.

Don't eat me!

Fright makes the essence qi descend, blocking the upper burner. As a result, the qi will go down to the lower burner, causing distention.

86

Winter comes so early this year!

See you next year, old chap.

Brothers, all get out of him!

Chill blocks the interstices, hampering the flowing of the nourishing qi and the defence qi. Hence "chill makes the qi contract".

Heat will open up the interstices and the pores, allowing the nourishing qi and the defence qi to flow out with sweat. Hence "heat makes the qi escape".

Being startled will cause palpitation. The spirit-mind will not be housed, and misgivings will prevail. Hence "being startled will make the qi scatter and become chaotic".

Overstraining will cause panting and sweating. Both the internal and external qi will run beyond the normal level. Hence "overstraining causes depletion of the qi".

What a heavy load!

He's carrying too much.

Excessive thought and obsession make the qi stagnant.

Treatise on Conditions of the Abdomen

In treating diseases in the abdomen, attention should be paid to the particular nature of different types of medicine, and meticulous care should be taken in judging the various symptoms.

原文：岐伯曰：夫芳草之气美，石药之气悍，二者其气急疾坚劲，故非缓心和人，不可以服此二者。帝曰：不可以服此二者，何以然？岐伯曰：夫热气剽悍，药气亦然，二者相遇，恐内伤脾。

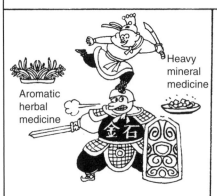

Aromatic herbal medicine

Heavy mineral medicine

金石

Qibo: Aromatic herbal medicines are mostly too dispersing, and heavy mineral medicines are mostly strong and harsh.

These two types of medicine are not suitable for people with a violent temper.

Unless the patient is of a calm and gentle nature, better avoid taking these two types of medicine.

Why are these two types of medicine not to be used?

Because heat conditions are harsh and the combination of the harsh condition and the harsh nature of the medicine will injure the spleen qi.

原文：有病膺肿，颈痛胸满腹胀，此为何病？何以得之？岐伯曰：名厥逆。……阳气重上，有余于上(之故)……何以知怀子之且生也？岐伯曰：身有病而无邪脉也。

The Yellow Emperor: What is the cause of pain and swelling in the neck coupled with fullness and distention in the chest and abdomen?

Ha! Ha!

Hee! Hee!

I just feel unwell.

Are you ill?

The Yellow Emperor: How can you tell whether a woman is pregnant or ill in the abdomen?

It looks like she's ill, but disease cannot be detected from her pulse. Congratulations! She's expecting!

Treatise on the Pathology of Wind

原文：风气藏于皮肤之间，内不得通，外不得
泄。风者善行而数变，腠理开，则洒然寒，闭
则热而闷。其寒也，则衰食饮；其热也，则消
肌肉。故使人怢慄而不能食，名曰寒热。风气
与阳明入胃，循脉而上至目内眦，其人肥，则
风气不得外泄，则为热中而目黄；人瘦则外泄
而寒，则为寒中而泣出。

风气与太阳俱入，行诸脉俞，散于分肉之间，
与卫气相干，其道不利，故使肌肉愤䐃而有疡
；卫气有所凝而不行，故其肉不仁也。疠者，
有荣气热腑，其气不清，故使其鼻柱坏而色败
，皮肤疡溃。风寒客于脉而不去，名曰疠风，
或名曰寒热。

Wind is the cause of many diseases. It is dynamic and changeable by nature. When it invades the body, there will be many pathological manifestations; for example fever, chills, leprosy, hemiplegia. In some cases, wind will penetrate deep into the body and cause damages to the viscera.

It spreads very quickly giving rise to a variety of symptoms.

This is wind evil.

When wind gets into the skin, it will prevent communication with the channels and collaterals and block dispersal at the surface.

How cold I am!

If the interstices and pores are loose and open, chill will be the result.

If the interstices and pores are compact and closed, fever and vexation will be the result.

In case of chill, the patient will have a poor appetite.

In the case of fever, the patient will be emaciated. Feeling cold prevents one from taking sufficient food, and this is called chill-fever.

When wind gets into the stomach through the yangming channel, it will follow the channel up to the eyes.

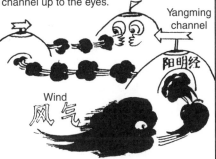

In the case of an obese person, the wind cannot disperse and builds up in the body, causing heat stroke and yellowing of the eyeballs.

In the case of a thin person, yang qi disperses from the body easily, causing cold stroke and constant tearing from the eyes.

When the wind invades the body through the greater yang channel and scatters in various channels, flesh and muscles, it will struggle with the defence qi causing obstruction of the channels that will give rise to swelling of the muscles and sores.

If there is stagnation of the defence qi, numbness and tingling will result.

Pestilential wind occurs when wind evil invades the channels, heating up and degenerating the nutrition qi. As a result, lesions and ulceration will develop on the nose.

That is caused by the invasion of wind cold and its subsequent lingering in the channels.

It is also known as cold heat as it is preceded with the symptom of fever and aversion to cold.

92

原文：以春甲乙伤于风者为肝风，以夏丙丁伤于风者为心风，以季夏戊己伤于邪者为脾风，以秋庚辛中于邪者为肺风，以冬壬癸中于邪者为肾风。

Being attacked by wind on the days of jia yi in spring is called liver wind, as the liver as well as the days jia yi and spring are associated with the element wood. Being attacked by wind on the days bing ding in summer is called heart wind, as the organ as well as the days and the season are associated with fire. Being attacked on the days wu ji in long summer is called spleen wind, as the relevant factors are all associated with the earth. Being attacked on the days geng xin in autumn is known as lung wind, as the relevant factors are all associated with metal. Being attacked on the days ren gui in winter is known as kidney wind, as the relevant factors are all associated with water.

The wind evil may get into the shuxue (transport points) of the five zang and six fu organs.

原文：风中五脏六腑之俞，亦为脏腑之风，各入其门户，所中则为偏风。

Transport points

We've made it.

俞穴

冲啊杀呀！

Charge! Charge!

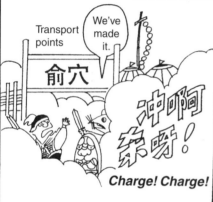

We've won the battle.

When it penetrates deep into the body, it is known as visceral wind.

It is known as one-sided wind when the invasion by wind takes place at one point or on one side of the body.

風邪
Wind evil

Help! Help!

What's wrong with you, my old man?

This side of my face is convulsive.

Wind evil invades the body from where the blood and qi are weak.

原文：风气循风府而上，则为脑风，风入系头，
则为目风，眼寒。
饮酒中风，则为漏风。
入房汗出中风，则为内风。
新沐中风，则为首风。
久风入中，则为肠风，飧泄。
外在腠理，则为泄风。
故风者，百病之长也，至其变化，乃为他病也，
无常方，然致有风气也。

When the wind attacks and gets into the fengfu (meaning wind house) channels, it will follow the channel up to the brain, known as brain wind.	When the wind gets into the head through the eyes, it is called eye wind, and the eyes will be averse to wind cold.

If the wind invades the body when one has been drinking alcohol, it is called leaky wind.	If the wind strikes when one is sweating from sex, it is called internal wind.

If the wind attacks when one has been having a shampoo, it is called head wind.

If the wind evil that has lingered in the flesh and interstices gets into the intestines, it is called intestinal wind and will cause diarrhoea.

The wind existing in the interstices causing spontaneous sweating is called discharge wind.

So wind is the main cause of many diseases.

The wind is quite changeable after getting into the body and there is no definite rule to the particular pathological manifestations it has. But the root cause is the invasion of the wind.

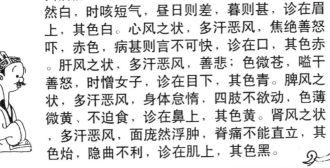

原文：五脏风之形状不同者何？愿闻其诊，及其病能。岐伯曰：肺风之状，多汗恶风，色皏然白，时咳短气，昼日则差，暮则甚，诊在眉上，其色白。心风之状，多汗恶风，焦绝善怒吓，赤色，病甚则言不可快，诊在口，其色赤。肝风之状，多汗恶风，善悲；色微苍，嗌干善怒，时憎女子，诊在目下，其色青。脾风之状，多汗恶风，身体怠惰，四肢不欲动，色薄微黄、不迫食，诊在鼻上，其色黄。肾风之状，多汗恶风，面庞然浮肿，脊痛不能直立，其色炲，隐曲不利，诊在肌上，其色黑。

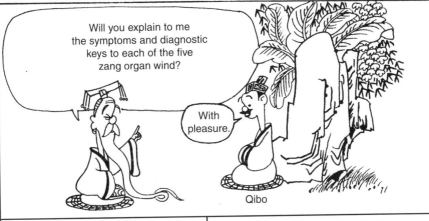

Will you explain to me the symptoms and diagnostic keys to each of the five zang organ wind?

With pleasure.

Qibo

Lung wind manifests itself in excessive sweating and aversion to wind. The patient is pale and susceptible to panting and coughing.

Always like this in the evening.

Ha ... choo ...!

The symptoms ease during the day but become more serious towards evening.

Heart wind manifests itself in excessive sweating and aversion to wind. There is depletion of body fluids and dryness of lips and tongue. The patient is red in the face and angers easily. Speech may be affected in serious cases.

The face is greenish blue and the throat is dry. The patient angers easily and is sometimes disgusted with people of the opposite sex.

How disgusting!

The manifestations of kidney wind are excessive sweating, aversion to wind, a dull greyed face and swelling of the eyes. The patient has pain in the spine and is unable to straighten.

I'm ill.

What's the matter with you, Mum?

Liver wind has the symptoms of profuse sweating and aversion to wind. The patient is susceptible to sadness and grief.

What a desolate scene! Leaves swept by autumn wind.

Spleen wind manifests itself in spontaneous sweating and aversion to wind. The patient, usually with a dull yellow in the face, has heavy limbs and gets tired easily.

Come and have lunch please!

I don't feel like eating.

The face may even be the shade of charcoal, and there may be obstruction of the urinary tract.

Is that me in the mirror?

原文：胃风之状，颈多汗，恶风，饮食不下，嗝塞不通，腹善胀，失衣则䐜胀，食寒则泄，诊形瘦而腹大。首风之状，头面多汗，恶风，当先风一日则病甚，头痛不可以出内，至其风日，则病少愈。漏风之状，或多汗，常不可单衣，食则汗出，甚则身汗，喘息恶风，衣常濡，口干善渴，不能劳事。泄风之状，多汗，汗出泄衣上，口中干，上渍其风，不能劳事，身体尽痛，则寒。帝曰：善。

For stomach wind, the manifestations are excessive sweating around the neck and aversion to wind.

Other symptoms are a lack of appetite, obstruction of the digestive tract and distention in the abdomen.

I won't eat any more.

Don't remove your clothes.

If the patient does not keep warm enough, there will be distention in the abdomen.

Consuming cold food will cause diarrhoea ...

I'm going to take a walk. Oh, so distended!

Ouch! It aches so much in the abdomen.

Head wind manifests itself in excessive sweating on the head and face with aversion to wind. The patient suffers a severe headache on the day preceding weather change.

However, the pain eases on the day the weather changes.

I feel better today.

Leaky wind manifests itself in aversion to wind and intermittent sweating. The patient should wear warm clothes.

Please put on another coat.

Thank you.

Sweating follows eating. In serious cases, the patient is often wet through with perspiration and is too weak for manual labour. Other symptoms are panting, thirst, and a dry mouth.

In discharge wind, the mouth is always dry and the skin always wet with excessive perspiration. The patient feels pain and chill all over and is unable to do manual labour.

Oh, I am in such pain!

Thank you for the illustrative explanations.

Yellow Emperor

Treatise on the Bi Symptoms

Bi refers to pain, numbness or other impediments caused by the invasion of wind, cold and damp. It is further divided into five types according to the particular season in which it occurs. The pathogen can also attack the relevant internal organs giving rise to various symptoms. If the nourishing qi and defence qi are in disorder, one will suffer from disease. However, so long as they do not combine with wind, cold and damp, the bi condition will not occur.

原文：帝曰：内舍五脏六腑，何气使然？岐伯曰：五脏皆有合，病久而不去者，内舍于其合也。故骨痹不已，复感于邪，内舍于肾；筋痹不已，复感于邪，内舍于肝；脉痹不已，复感于邪，内舍于心；脾痹不已，复感于邪，内舍于脾；皮痹不已，复感于邪，内舍于肺；所谓痹者，各以其时重感于风寒湿之气也。

The Yellow Emperor: How is it that the bi pathogen can also stagnate within the five zang and six fu organs?

Well, it is a good place to settle down in.

内脏

The zang organs

Qibo: The five zang organs are connected with the relevant channels. If the bi pathogen lingers on the surface, it will invade the corresponding organs.

It will make a very good bed.

肾

The kidneys

If the bone bi lingers, the evil qi will invade the kidneys.

If the tendon bi lingers, the evil qi will invade the liver.

What a cozy home!

肝

The liver

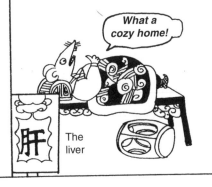

If the vein bi lingers, the evil qi will invade the heart.

If the muscle bi lingers, the evil qi will invade the spleen.

The various bi diseases are caused by wind, cold, and damp that invade the body in different seasons.

Qibo

If the skin bi lingers, the evil qi will invade the lungs.

原文：凡痹之客五脏者，肺痹者，烦满喘而呕；心痹者，脉不通，烦则心下鼓，暴上气而喘，嗌干善噫，厥气上则恐；肝痹者，夜卧则惊多饮，数小便，上为引如怀；肾痹者，善胀，尻以代踵，脊以代头；脾痹者，四肢解堕，发咳呕汁，上为大塞；肠痹者，数饮而出不得，中气喘争，时发飧泄；胞痹者，少腹膀胱按之内痛，若沃以汤，涩于小便，上为清涕。

Different symptoms manifest when the bi disease invades different organs; the manifestations of lung bi are vexation and fullness in the chest, coupled with panting and vomiting.

Heart bi manifests itself as obstruction of the blood flow, vexation, panting, dry throat, belching, and fright.

Liver bi manifests itself as being repeatedly jolted awake, frequent thirst and urination.

The disease develops from the ribs to the lower abdomen with swelling as if one is pregnant.

103

In the case of kidney bi, the symptoms are distended abdomen, weak bones, inability to walk, contracted body unable to straighten and a hunch higher than the head.

For spleen bi, the symptoms are weak limbs, lack of strength, coughing, vomiting of clear liquids, and even obstruction above the diaphragm.

Tchac!

For intestinal bi, there is inhibition of urination though the patient drinks water frequently.

The yang qi and evil qi in the intestines and the stomach battle against each other, sometimes causing excessive excretion of undigested food.

Charge! Charge!

In the case of bladder bi, the patient feels pain from pressure in the lower abdomen as if the bladder is filled with hot water.

There are also burning urination and clear nasal discharge.

原文：阴气者，静则神藏，躁则消亡。
饮食自倍，肠胃乃伤。
淫气喘息，痹聚在肺；淫气忧思，痹聚在心
；淫气遗溺，病聚在肾；淫气乏竭，痹聚在
肝；淫气肌绝，痹聚在脾。诸痹不已，亦益
内也。其风气胜者，其人易已也。

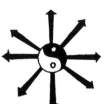

In peace and tranquillity, the yin qi in the zang organs is properly stored and nurtured; when agitated, it will disperse and even be depleted.

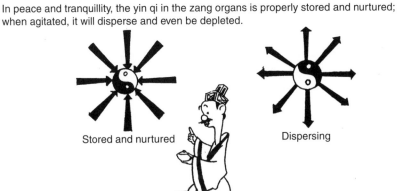

Stored and nurtured

Dispersing

Overeating will injure the stomach and intestines.

Good heavens! You're still eating.

It is bi in the lungs in the case of evil qi causing panting.

It is bi in the heart in the case of evil qi causing worries and grief.

It is bi in the kidneys in the case of evil qi causing bed-wetting.

Oh, I've wetted the bed again.

It is the bi in the liver in the case of evil qi causing extreme exhaustion

It is bi in the spleen in the case of evil qi causing emaciation of flesh.

If diseases of various bi linger they may develop from the exterior to the interior of the body. When the bi is caused predominantly by wind, there is a better chance of getting cured.

Poor boy, you've just died for a passer-by.

So he's died for my sake.

原文：荣卫之气，亦令人痹乎？岐伯曰：荣者水谷之精气也，和调于五脏，洒陈于六腑，乃能入于脉也。故循脉上下贯五脏，络六腑也。卫者水谷之悍气也。其气悍疾滑利，不能入于脉。故循皮肤之中，分肉之间，熏于盲膜，散于胸腹，逆其气则病，从其气则愈，不与风、寒、湿气合，故不为痹。

The Yellow Emperor asked:

Can the nourishing qi and defence qi also cause bi diseases?

Qibo: The nourishing qi is the essence extracted from water and food.

Nourishing Qi

Water and Food

It is harmonized in the five zang organs and distributed in the six fu organs.

It then follows the channels throughout the body, nourishing and connecting the five zang and six fu organs.

Nourishing qi

It circulates in the skin and muscles, distributing in the chest and abdomen.

So long as their harmony and regular flow are restored, the patient will be cured.

The defence qi is also extracted from water and food. It is fierce by nature and travels fast and smooth, unable to get into vessels and channels.

If nourishing qi and defence qi lose their balance and harmony, disease will occur.

Generally speaking, diseases of bi will not occur so long as the nourishing qi and the defence qi are not combined with wind, cold or damp.

原文：黄帝问曰：痹之安生？岐伯对曰：风寒湿三气杂至，合而为痹也。其风气胜者为行痹；寒气胜者为痛痹，湿气胜者为著痹也。
帝曰：其有五者何也？岐伯曰：以冬遇此者为骨痹；以春遇此者为筋痹；以夏遇此者为脉痹；以至阴遇此者为肌痹，以秋遇此者为皮痹。

The Yellow Emperor: What are the causes of bi diseases?

Ouch!

风　　寒　　湿
Wind　Cold　Damp

Qibo: As wind, cold and damp attack in turn or strike in alliance, diseases of bi will occur.

109

110

Treatise on the Syndrome of Wilting

The wilting condition starts in the lungs, the highest organ of the body and a distribution center. When the lungs are attacked by heat, a dry wilting will develop. When the liver is attacked by heat, a tendon wilting will occur. When the spleen is attacked by heat, flesh and muscle wilting will result. When the kidneys are attacked by heat, it will cause bone wilting.

原文：帝曰：何以得之？岐伯曰：肺者胜之长也，为心之盖也，有所失亡，所求不得，则发肺鸣，鸣则肺热叶焦，故曰：五脏因肺热叶焦，发为痿躄，此之谓也。悲哀太甚，则胞络绝，胞络绝，则阳气内动，发则心下崩数溲血也。故《本病》曰：大经空虚，发为肌痹传为脉痿。思想无穷，所愿不得，意淫于外，入房太甚，宗筋驰纵，发为筋痿，及为白淫。

The Yellow Emperor: How is wilting caused?

Qibo: The lungs are the highest of all the organs and also serve as the canopy of the heart.

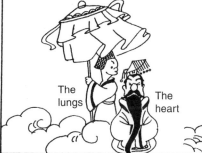

The lungs

The heart

When one is sad because of failure to fulfill one's wish, the qi in the lungs will not flow smoothly. Heat will build up and the lobes of the lungs will be atrophied.

I really cannot afford to grant your wishes for all these.

But you promised me!

Therefore, the five zang viscera develop into crippling wilting because of lung heat scorching the lobes.

Excessive grief will injure the pericardiac network resulting in obstruction of the flowing of the heart qi. The frenetic stirring of the yang qi in the heart will force the blood to go down, giving rise to blood in the urine.

The case seems to be quite serious.

So it is recorded in the book "*The Origin of Diseases*" that major channel vessel emptiness leads to muscle impediment which in the end develops into vessel wilting.

The Origin of Diseases

Indulgence in flights of fancy that cannot be realized, lured by carnal desire and taxed by excessive sex, one will develop sluggishness in the ancestral sinew which will develop into tendon wilting resulting in strangely turbid or white vaginal discharge.

原文：故《下经》曰：筋痿者，生于肝，使内也。有渐于湿，以水为事，若有所留，居处相湿，肌肉濡渍，痹而不仁，发为肉痿。故《下经》曰：肉痿者，得之湿地也。有所远行劳倦，逢大热而渴，渴则阳气内伐，内伐则热舍于肾，肾者水藏也，今水不皮火，则骨枯而髓虚，故足不任身，发为骨痿。故《下经》曰：骨痿者，生于大热也。

Tendon wilting results from the liver being attacked by heat, and from overindulgence in sex that injures the internal essence qi.

You should read this *Medicine Classic* carefully.

Papa, take a good rest!

If one is often exposed to damp, e.g., working in water, damp will build up in the body.

Or if one lives in a damp environment, the flesh and muscles will be affected by the damp evil, causing persistent numbness and ultimately developing into wilting. Hence, the *Medicine Classic* says wilting of the flesh and muscles is caused by prolonged exposure to a damp environment.

Fatigue from long travel in intense hot weather will cause thirst that in turn will give rise to excessive yang qi, and the accumulated heat will attack the kidneys.

The kidney is the organ for water. If water cannot prevail over the fiery heat, the bone and marrow will become withered and cannot support the body. This is known as wilting of the bone.

Treatise on Unusual Diseases

There are some unusual diseases such as persistent distention in the chest and ribs, swelling of the hips and legs, loss of voice in the ninth month of pregnancy, persistent headache for several years, sweet or bitter taste in the mouth, innate epilepsy etc. Special care should be taken in treating these diseases.

原文：帝曰：病胁下满气逆，二三岁不已，是为何病？岐伯曰：病名曰息积，此不妨于食，不可炙刺，积为导引服药，药不能独治也。帝曰：人有身体髀股胻皆肿，环脐而痛，是为何病？岐伯曰：病名曰伏梁，此风根也。其气溢于大肠而著于肓，肓之原在脐下，故环脐而痛也。不可动之，动之为水溺涩之病也。

A patient may feel fullness and distention in the chest and ribs coupled with panting, and the symptoms can persist for two or three years. What kind of disease is it?

Qibo: This is called breath accumulation, and it does not affect eating or drinking, moxibustion or acupuncture are definitely not to be used in treatment.

Medicinal herbs alone cannot cure the disease but should be applied in addition to the method of conduction which is able to free the stagnation of qi and blood.

It's time to have medicine.

The Yellow Emperor: What is the condition of swelling hips and legs with pain around the navel?

116

原文：黄帝问曰：人有重身，九月而喑，此为何也？岐伯对曰：胞之络脉绝也。

帝曰：何以言之？岐伯曰：胞络者，系于肾，少阴之脉贯肾，系舌本故不能言。

帝曰：治之奈何？岐伯曰：无治也，当十月复。刺法曰：无损不足，益有余。

The Yellow Emperor: Why do some women lose their voice in the ninth month of pregnancy?

Oh, you can't speak!

XXXX XXXX

Qibo: That is caused by the obstruction of the collaterals of the uterus as a result of the constriction of the fetus.

It doesn't matter.

The disease does not need any treatment, as the patient will recover her voice after delivery of the baby, which will remove the constriction on the uterus collaterals.

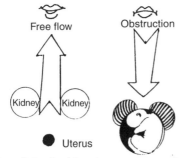

Free flow

Obstruction

Kidney Kidney

● Uterus

The collaterals of the uterus are connected to the kidneys whose channel goes upward to the root of the tongue. That is why speech may be impaired.

Really, she's well again.

原文：帝曰：人有病头痛，以数岁不已，此安得之，名为何病？岐伯曰：当有所犯大寒，内至骨髓，髓者以脑为主，脑逆，故令头痛，齿亦痛，病名厥逆。

The Yellow Emperor: How is it that some patients have persistent headache that may last several years?

Qibo: That is caused by severe cold which penetrates into the bone marrow and travels upward to the brain.

Ouch! My teeth hurt like this.

Headache and toothache will result from that, which is termed reverse flow.

原文：帝曰：有病口甘者，病名为何？何以得之？岐伯曰：此五气之溢也，名曰脾瘅。夫五味入口，藏于胃，脾为之行其精气津液在脾，故令人口甘也，此肥美之所发也，此人必数食甘美而多肥也，肥者，令人内热，甘者令人中满，故其气上溢，转为消渴。治之以兰，除陈气也。

The Yellow Emperor: How is it that some people have a sweet taste in their mouth?

How queer! There's a sweet taste!

How come?

I've carried today's food here, sir.

I've noted it down.

Sugar content 80%

Stomach

The food is received and stored in the stomach.

The spleen

But the spleen is to extract the essence of the food and distribute it throughout the body.

Now the heat in the spleen causes the food essence to stagnate in the organ which has its opening in the mouth. Hence the sweet taste.

This disease results from the patient's indulgence in rich food.

I see.

How enjoyable to have sweet refreshments!

What a terrible heat!

The sweet taste can cause fullness and distention in the chest and the abdomen. The disease caused by the upward flow of the essence qi on account of spleen dysfunction is termed wasting thirst.

Rich food will give rise to heat in the body.

For treatment, fragrant thoroughwort is to be used to remove the stagnation of heat. This is one of the 13 prescriptions of the *Medicine Classic*.

Qibo

原文：帝曰：有病口苦，取阳陵泉。口苦者，病名为何？何以得之？岐伯曰：病名曰胆瘅。夫肝者，中之将也，取决于胆，咽为之使，此人者，数谋虑不决，故胆虚。气上逆而口为之苦。

The Yellow Emperor: What is the disease of bitter taste in the mouth?

Please explain its cause.

This is gallbladder heat.

It's just like having tasted the bile.

The throat is controlled by the liver; the organ with the general's position, whose function is dependent on the gallbladder; the organ with the position of the justice official.

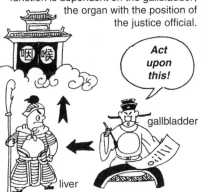

Act upon this!

gallbladder

liver

The patient is preoccupied with worries and is very indecisive, which spoils the function of the gallbladder. The bile, instead of being distributed properly, spills upward, resulting in a bitter taste in the mouth.

I see ...

121

原文：帝曰：人生而有病癫疾者，病名曰何？安所得之？岐伯曰：病名为胎病，此得之在母腹中时，其母有所大惊，气上而不下，精气并居，故令子发为癫疾也。

The Yellow Emperor: How come some people are born with epilepsy?

This is a fetal illness. The mother must have experienced severe fright or shock.

This causes the qi to go upward instead of downward and the essence of qi to congeal instead of getting dispersed.

All these affect the normal development of the fetus, and consequently the child is born with epilepsy.

Treatise on Essentials of Diseases and their Therapy

People and nature are inseparable. The atmospheric influences in nature form the basis for illnesses in people. In case chaos occurs in these influences, the balance in the body will be disturbed resulting in illness. Medicine opposite in property to the invading pathogenic influence is to be used to restore balance, i.e. to cure the illness. So be sure to find out the true nature of the disease before resorting to any treatment.

原文：帝曰：善。火热，复恶寒发热，有如疟状，或一日发，或间数日发，其故何也？岐伯曰：胜复之气，会遇之时，有多少也。阴气多而阳气少，则其发日远；阳气多而阴气少，则其发日近。此胜复相薄，盛衰之节，疟亦同法。

The fire heat disease, i.e. repeated aversion to cold and running a fever, may attack periodically like malaria, either once a day or once a few days. What is the reason?

I can't bear the heat!

That depends on the relative amount of yin qi and yang qi when the prevalence qi and the retaliatory qi meet.

When yin qi exceeds yang qi, the period of attack is longer; when yang qi exceeds yin qi, the period of attack is shorter.

Yin

Yang

Charge! Charge! Charge!

The battle between the prevalence qi and the retaliatory qi is the key to cold and heat as well as to exuberance and debilitation. The same is true for the occurrence of malaria.

帝曰：善。方制君臣何谓也？岐伯曰：主病之谓君，佐君之谓臣，应臣之为谓使。非上下三品之谓也。

The Yellow Emperor: Please explain the sovereign medicine, minister medicine, and envoy medicine.

Qibo: The medicine that plays the major role in treating the disease is called the sovereign medicine.

SOVEREIGN

MINISTER

What serves as adjuvant to the sovereign medicine is called minister medicine.

What responds to the minister medicine is called envoy medicine.

ENVOY

Charge! Kill!

The three types are just a way of classifying medicines based on their respective role and nature.

原文：帝曰：五味阴阳之用何如？岐伯曰：辛甘发散为阳，酸苦涌泄为阴，咸味涌泄为阴，淡味涌为阳。六者或收或散，或缓或急，或燥或润，或䏏或坚，以所利而行之，调其气使其平也。

The role and nature of different flavours of herbal medicines

Medicines of an acrid or sweet flavour are yang in nature and have an effusing and dissipating effect.

Medicines of a sour or bitter flavour are yin in nature and have an upwelling and discharging effect.

Medicines of a salty flavour are yin in nature and have an upwelling and discharging effect.

Medicines of a bland flavour are yang in nature and have a percolating and draining effect.

The above medicines of different flavours are either contracting or dissipating; either moderate or fulminant; either dry or moistening; either soft or hard. It is necessary to choose the appropriate type according to the specific condition of illness so as to harmonize the qi and the blood for the restoration of balance in the body.

125

The Pathology Of Various Diseases

原文：帝曰：愿闻病机何如？岐伯曰：诸风掉眩皆属于肝；诸寒收引，皆属于肾；诸气膹郁，皆属于肺；诸湿肿满皆属于脾；诸热瞀瘛皆属于火；诸痛痒疮，皆属于心；诸厥固泄皆属于下；诸痿喘呕，皆属于上；诸禁鼓栗，如丧神守，皆属于火；诸痉项强，皆属于湿；诸逆冲上，皆属于火；诸胀腹大，皆属于热；诸躁狂越，皆属于火；诸暴强直，皆属于风；诸病有声，鼓之如鼓，皆属于热；诸病胕肿，痛酸惊骇，皆属于火；诸转反戾，水液浑浊，皆属于热；诸病水液，澄彻清冷，皆属于寒；诸呕吐酸，暴注下迫，皆属于热。故（大要）曰：谨守病机，各司其属。有者求之，无者求之，盛者责之，虚者责之。必先五胜，疏其血气，令其调达，而致和平。此之谓也。

Unsteady

I'm too dizzy to tell the direction.

Qibo: Diseases caused by wind such as tremor, dizziness, and vertigo are associated with the liver.

Where is it?

Come on! Massage my ailing spot.

Diseases caused by cold such as contraction and spasms are associated with the kidneys.

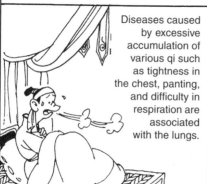

Diseases caused by excessive accumulation of various qi such as tightness in the chest, panting, and difficulty in respiration are associated with the lungs.

Diseases caused by damp such as bloating and distention are associated with the spleen.

127

Diseases of upward counterflow of the qi are associated with fire.

Diseases of abdominal distention and swelling are associated with heat.

Diseases of abnormal agitation and mania are associated with fire.

Diseases such as sudden attack of rigidity are associated with wind.

If the abdomen sounds like a drum when percussed, the diseases are associated with heat.

Diseases like puffy swelling, soreness, palpitations due to fright are associated with fire.

Treatise on Exuberance and Debilitation

Deficiency and excess in the qi of the organs may find expression in dreams indicating the state of energy in the body. In the case of excess, it is necessary to find out what is deficient for comprehensive diagnosis and treatment, and vice versa.

原文：是以少气之厥，令人妄梦，其极至迷。是以肺气虚则使人梦见白物，见人斩血藉藉。得其时则梦见兵战。

肾气虚，则使人梦见舟船溺人，得其时则梦伏水中，若有畏恐。肝气虚，则梦见菌香生草，得其时则梦伏树下不敢起。心气虚，则梦救火阳物，得其时则梦燔灼。脾气虚，则梦饮食不足，得其时则梦筑垣盖屋。

Reversal of qi of a vacuity type will cause the patient have wild dreams. In serious reversal, the dreams may be confusingly wild and beyond imagination.

How can it be like that?

In the case of qi deficiency of the lungs (associated with metal), one tends to dream of white objects and tragic, even murderous events.

In the case of excessive metal, one tends to dream of battles going on.

In the case of deficient qi in the kidneys (associated with water), one tends to dream of a sinking boat and a drowning person.

LINGSHU

Lingshu, or "Miraculous Pivot", is the other component part of "*The Yellow Emperor's Medicine Classic*". It follows the same theoretical system of Chinese medicine as Suwen or "Plain Questions", but is mainly on acupuncture and moxibustion, channels and collaterals, acupuncture points, nourishing and defence qi and blood.

Lingshu

Treatise On The Root Spirit

Spirit (shen), reflection (yi), ethereal soul (hun), corporeal soul (po), and will (zhi) are stored respectively in the heart, the spleen, the liver, the lungs, and the kidneys. Injury to them will cause diseases and may even lead to death.

原文：心怵惕思虑则伤神，神伤则恐惧自失，破胭脱肉，毛悴色夭，死于冬。脾愁忧而不解则伤意，意伤则悗乱，四肢不举，毛悴色夭死于春。肝悲哀动中则伤魂，魂伤则狂妄不精，不精则不正，当人阴缩而挛筋，两肋骨不举，毛悴色夭，死于秋。

The spirit is stored in the heart and will be injured by fear, fright, or excessive thoughts and worries.

I am afraid some mishap may happen to him.

If the spirit is injured, one tends to have groundless panic and worries and is often at a loss for the right ideas and decisions.

There's no more hope.

In a persistent case, the muscles of the limbs will be emaciated, the skin and hair will be wan and sallow, and the patient may die in winter.

Stop nagging me!

Mummy!

Reflection is stored in the spleen and will be injured by excessive anxiety and worries.

Injury to reflection will lead to groundless moodiness and vexation. In a persistent case, there will be impediment to the movement of the limbs, and the skin and hair will be wan and sallow.

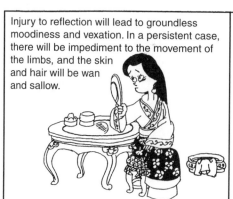

The patient may die in spring.

The ethereal soul is stored in the liver and will be injured by excessive sorrow and grief that affect the zang organs.

Injuring the ethereal soul will lead to slowness in the mind, abnormal speech and behaviour, and even derangement.

In a persistent case, the genitals will atrophy, the veins will be hypertonic, the ribs will be sunken, and the skin and hair will be wan and sallow. The patient may die in autumn.

134

原文：肺喜乐无极则伤魄，伤魄则狂，狂者意不存人，皮革焦，毛悴色夭死于夏。肾盛怒不止则伤志，志伤则喜忘其前言，腰脊不可以俯仰屈伸，毛悴色夭死于夏季。恐惧而不解则伤精，精伤则骨痿厥，精时自下。是故五脏主藏精者也，不可伤，伤则失守而阴虚；阴虚则无气，无气则死矣。

Fan Jin

The corporeal soul is stored in the lungs and will be injured by excessive joy and exhilaration.

I have passed!

If the corporeal soul is injured, one tends to lose self-control and go mad.

That is why the butcher Hu was able to cure the madness of his son-in-law Fan Jin with a slap in the face.

In a persistent case, the skin and hair will become wan and sallow.

I have passed! I ...

You have dashed my joy!

The patient may die in summer.

The will is stored in the kidneys and can be injured by violent rage.

You have again reduced my salary. I'll never forgive you, damned emperor!

Injury to the will can make one forget what he has said.

Did I ...

What audacity! You even dare to abuse his majesty!

Excessive grief and fear will injure the defence qi.

What a terrible dream!

In a persistent case, there will be impediment to the movement of the waist and back. The skin and hair will become wan and sallow, and the patient may die in summer.

If the essence qi is injured, there will be soreness in the joints, and weakness and reversal cold in the feet, accompanied with seminal emission and efflux.

I need to see the doctor.

As the zang organs are for restoring the essence of qi, injury to them will cause qi dispersal and loss, leading to yin vacuity which in turn will hinder qi transformation and over time will exhaust the qi in the organs and may even cause death.

Treatise on the Nourishing and Defence Qi

The essence qi of the body is transformed from food and drinks which have been digested in the stomach. It comprises of two types: the clear qi which is termed nourishing qi and the turbid qi which is termed defence qi. They circulate throughout the body and provide a guarantee of efficient physiological functions. Abnormality in the nourishing qi and the circulation of the defence qi will cause dysfunction of the body.

原文：岐伯曰：人受气于谷，谷入于胃，以传于肺，五脏六腑，皆以受气，其清者为营，浊者为卫，营在脉中，卫在脉外，营周不休。

Qibo: The essence qi of the body is transformed from food and drinks.

The lungs (the premier)

The composition of the essence is fully up to standard.

The stomach (granary official)

Food and drinks are received and digested by the stomach. Their essence is transported to the lungs.

I'll keep a little for myself.

Fair enough! The intestines, heart, liver stomach, spleen, lungs, have each got their proper share.

The five zang and six fu organs are thus all nourished by the essence qi.

The clear qi is called nourishing qi, and the turbid qi is called defence qi.

Nourishing qi

Defence qi.

The former circulates in the vessels and the latter outside the vessels.

Both are constantly flowing throughout the body.

137

原文：黄帝曰：老人之不夜瞑者，何气使然？
少壮之人不昼瞑者，何气使然？岐伯答曰：壮
者之气血盛，其肌肉滑，气道通，营卫之行，
不偺其常，故昼精而夜瞑，老者之气血衰，其
肌肉枯，气道涩，五脏之气相搏，其营气衰少
而卫内伐，故昼不精，夜不瞑。

The Yellow Emperor: Why can't older people sleep soundly at night?

What time is it, old man?

It's already one o'clock.

And why can't people in the prime of their life sleep soundly during the day?

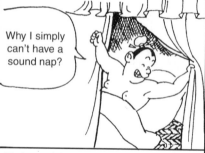

Why I simply can't have a sound nap?

What prodigious strength! Great!

Qibo: The qi and blood of people in their prime are exuberant, their qi channels are clear and their muscles smooth.

Their nourishing qi and defence qi are flowing and functioning properly, enabling them to sleep soundly at night.

Z z z...

138

139

原文：黄帝曰：人有热饮食下胃，其气未定，汗则出，或出于面，或出于背，或出于半身，其不循卫气之道而出，何也？岐伯曰：此外伤于风，内开腠理，毛蒸理泄，卫气走之，故不得循其道。此气剽悍滑疾，见开而出，故不得从其道，故命曰漏泄。

The Yellow Emperor: Sometimes, people begin to perspire before hot food and drink are digested by the stomach and transformed into essence qi.

I'm all wet on the back.

I'm already spouting sweat!

So hot!

Some perspire in the face, some in the back, and some around the waist. Why doesn't the sweat come out along the course of the flow of the defence qi?

We have hit the target.

Wind Evil

Qibo: That is caused by the external contraction of wind evil. The exterior vacuity has made the body surface insecure.

140

Internally, the fuming and steaming of the hot food and drink cause the interstices to open. Heat evaporates from the pores and sweat is discharged through the slack interstices.

The defence qi is intrepid and slippery by nature. It travels fast and instead of following the normal course, will get out if gaps and openings are available in the muscles and on the skin.

原文：黄帝曰：人饮酒，酒亦入胃，谷未熟，而小便独先下，何也？岐伯答曰：酒者，熟谷之液也，其气悍以清，故后谷而入，先谷而液出焉。黄帝曰：善。余闻上焦如雾，中焦如沤，下焦如渎，此之谓也。

The Yellow Emperor: When one drinks liquor, alcohol gets into the stomach together with food.

But why is urine discharged before the food is digested?

Qibo: Alcohol is the liquid from fermented grains. It has a sharp smell, and moves smooth and fast.

Toilet

So alcohol is transformed into urine and discharged before food is digested.

Very illustrative explanation!

The Yellow Emperor: The qi of the upper burner spreads on and envelops the whole body like fog.

Mummy, let me have a taste of the delicious pickles.

Fine, the water is all drained!

The middle burner digests and absorbs the nourishment of the food like water soaking things.

The function of the lower burner is, like drains, used to discharge the dregs and waste liquid accumulated after digestion and absorption.

Treatise on Medical Advice

People who cannot follow the direct advice of doctors should pay particular attention to the temperature of their food and clothing. A harmonious medium of heat and cold will enable the original qi to prevail in the interior and exterior of the body and to protect it from the invasion of the evil qi.

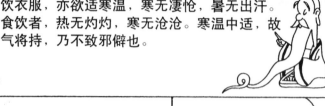

原文：便其相逆者奈何？岐伯曰：便此者，食饮衣服，亦欲适寒温，寒无凄怆，暑无出汗。食饮者，热无灼灼，寒无沧沧。寒温中适，故气将持，乃不致邪僻也。

What is the proper way to maintain good health especially for those who cannot follow the direct advice of doctors?

They can follow some expedient ways but there should be a proper limit in what they do.

In eating and dressing, be sure to maintain the right temperature.

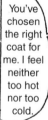

You've chosen the right coat for me. I feel neither too hot nor too cold.

If a patient prefers to be cold, he should only be exposed to moderate cold, and in no case should he feel chilly.

Stay in the cold for a while. Didn't you complain it's too hot?

I'm chilled to death.

145

Treatise On The Six Types Of Qi

There are six types of qi in the body: jing, qi, jin, humour, blood, and vein. They are each associated with a particular organ and their vacuity will lead to different pathoconditions.

原文：黄帝曰：余闻人有精、气、津、液、血、脉，余意以为一气耳，今乃辨为六名，余不知其所以然。岐伯曰：两神相搏，合而成形，常先身生，是谓精。何谓气？岐伯曰：上焦开发，宣五谷味，薰肤，充身，泽毛，若雾露之溉，是谓气。何谓津？岐伯曰：腠理发泄汗出溱溱，是谓津。何谓液？岐伯曰：谷入气满，淖泽注于骨，骨属屈伸，泄泽补益脑髓，皮肤润泽，是谓液。何谓血？岐伯曰：中焦受气，取汁，变化而赤，是谓血。何谓脉？岐伯曰：壅遏营气，令无所避，是谓脉。

Jing

Qi

Jin

Vein

Blood

Humour

The Yellow Emperor:
In my opinion, jing, qi, jin, humour, blood, and vein are simply qi in essence. Why is it classified into six types?

Qibo: Sexual intercourse will conceive new life. The primordial matter before the formation of new life is called jing.

It is also called zygote.

146

The essence of food and drinks is distributed by the upper burner to warm the skin, enrich and moisten the hair, and nourish the body as rain and dew irrigate the plants. That is called qi.

Upper Burner 上焦

The sweat effused from the interstices is termed jin fluids.

The essence qi transformed from food and drink in the stomach is distributed throughout the body. The thick, turbid, and slippery part of it percolates to the bones to lubricate the movement of the joints.

The machine needs lubrication just like the human brain.

And it also enriches and nourishes the *"brain marrow" and moistens the skin. Such thick, turbid and slippery matter is called humour.

The red liquid transformed from the essence of food and grain accepted by the middle burner is blood.

Traffic and pedestrians, keep in your own lane.

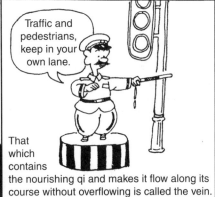

That which contains the nourishing qi and makes it flow along its course without overflowing is called the vein.

The Chinese refer to brain matter as "brain marrow". This is due to the fact that insufficient bone marrow may lead to tinnitus, vertigo and listlessness; all maladies of the brain.

原文：黄帝曰：六气者，有余不足，气之多少，脑髓之虚实，血脉之清浊，何以知之？岐伯曰：精脱者，耳聋；气脱者，目不明；津脱者，腠理开，汗大泄；液脱者，骨属屈伸不利，色夭，脑髓消，胫酸，耳数鸣；血脱者，色白，夭然不泽，其脉空虚，此其候也。

Blood

Humour

Jin

脉 Vein

气 Qi

精 Jing

Jing, qi, jin, humour, blood, and vein may be in surplus or insufficient. How can one know the repletion and vacuity of the brain marrow, and the clearness and turbidity of blood?.

How deaf!

What? Didn't quite catch you.

Qibo: Jing vacuity will cause difficulty in hearing.

Why? All the words are blurred.

Qi vacuity will cause difficulty in sight.

原文：六气者，贵贱如何？岐伯曰：六气者，各有部主也，其贵贱善恶，可为常主，然五谷与胃为大海也。

What is the order of the six types of qi in terms of importance?

Have some refreshments before dinner!

Jing

qi

jin

Jing, qi, jin, humour, blood, and vessel are each associated with a particular organ.

Irrespective of seniority or juniority, they are regularly associated with a particular organ, and all find their source of food and drinks digested in the stomach.

humour

The five zang organs and the six fu organs are stored safely in the chest and abdomen in proper order just as valuables are stored in a coffer.

blood

vessel

Treatise on the Four Seas*

There are four seas in the body: the sea of qi, the sea of blood, the sea of grain and water, and the sea of marrow. Excess or deficiency of each of the four seas will lead to different symptoms.

原文：黄帝曰：四海之逆顺奈何？岐伯曰：气海有余者，气满胸中，悗息面赤，气海不足，则气少不足以言。血海有余，则常想其身大，怫然不知其所病：血海不足，亦常想其身小，狭然不知其所病。水谷之海有余，则腹满；水谷之海不足，则饥不栖谷食。髓海有余，则转劲多力，自过其度。髓海不足，则脑转耳鸣，胫酸眩冒，目无所见懈怠安卧。

The chest centre is the confluence of qi and is called the sea of qi.

The Yellow Emperor: Please explain the normal function and dysfunction of the four seas?

邪气

Evil Qi

Deficiency of the sea of qi means vacuity of the lung qi which will lead to weak and short breath, and listlessness in speech.

Qibo: Excess of the sea of qi means exuberance of evil qi which will lead to suppressed breathing, vexation, panting, and a flushed face.

*The four seas is an analogy of various biological systems functioning in our body. For example, the sea of grain and water refers to the digestive system and correspondingly, the sea of blood refers to the circulatory system.

The twelve channel vessels are the confluence of blood and are called the sea of blood. In case of its excess, one will feel his body distended and heavy. He will be irritable without knowing where the ailment is.

Damn it!

Deficiency of the sea of blood will make the patient feel his body empty and small. He will be gloomy without knowing where the ailment is.

What illness is this?

Food and drinks converge in the stomach which is therefore called the sea of grain and water. Excess of it will lead to bloating of the stomach duct and abdomen.

Stop kidding!

Daddy, your stomach and abdomen are simply like this drum.

152

In the case of a deficient sea of grain and water, the patient does not feel like eating though hungry.

The brain is the confluence of the marrow and is called the *sea of marrow. In the case of a sufficiency of the sea of marrow, one's movement will be more agile and more energetic than normal people.

Deficiency of the sea of marrow will give rise to tinnitus, dizziness, weak legs, and failing of sight. One may have a feeling of spinning in the head.

And one may be dispirited and drowsy most of the time.

Why are you so listless?

Don't bother me!

*Refer to page 147.

Treatise on Distention

When the defence qi and the nourishing qi operate normally, digestion and nourishing will be go on properly. If their normal flow is affected, there will be battling between the essence qi and the cold evil, resulting in distention.

原文：黄帝曰：胀者焉生？何因而有？岐伯曰：卫气之在身也，常然并脉，循分肉，行有逆顺，阴阳相随，乃得天和，五脏更始，四时循序，五谷乃化。然后厥气在下，营卫留止寒气逆上，真邪相攻，二气相搏，乃合为胀也。

Oh, the abdomen is distended like a drum.

The Yellow Emperor: What is the cause of the disease distention?

Where are you going?

Let's go together.

Qibo: The defence qi flows outside the vessels along with the blood in normal conditions.

I eat when hungry and go to bed when sleepy.

In cooperation with the nourishing qi, it circulates and operates in proper laws of yin and yang day and night keeping the body in good health.

The Five Zang Organs

In the body, the nourishing qi and the defence qi nourish and protect the zang organs and guarantee the transformation of the essence of food and drinks.

And they adapt their circulation and operation to the changes of the seasons, keeping the body and nature in good harmony.

Charge!

Cold evil

You disgusting robber, get out of my way quickly!

Essence qi

If the reverse qi remains in the lower part of the body affecting their normal operation and the cold qi flows reversely upward, the essence qi and the cold evil struggle against each other resulting in distention.

155

Treatise On The Relation Between The Viscera And The Five Sense Organs

The five sense organs on the head are related to the zang viscera: the nose to the lungs, the eyes to the liver, the lips to the spleen, the tongue to the heart, and the ears to the kidneys.

原文：黄帝曰：愿闻五官。岐伯曰：鼻者，肺
之官也；目者，肝之官也；口唇者，脾之官也
；舌者，心之官也；耳者，肾之官也。

The Yellow Emperor: Please explain the relation between the five sense organs and the zang viscera?

Qibo: The nose in charge of respiration is associated with the lungs.

The eyes in charge of identifying the five colours are associated with the liver.

The lips in charge of receiving food and drinks are associated with the spleen.

The ears in charge of hearing are associated with the kidney.

The lungs

The liver

The heart

The spleen

The kidneys

The tongue in charge of identifying the five flavours is associated with the heart.

Treatise On Bravery

The physical characteristics of the body such as the colour and thickness of the skin, the texture of the muscles, the size and shape of the organs etc. are closely related with one's susceptibility to illness and are important factors in deciding whether one is brave or timid.

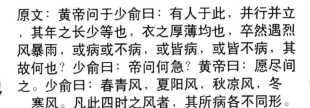

原文：黄帝问于少俞曰：有人于此，并行并立，其年之长少等也，衣之厚薄均也，卒然遇烈风暴雨，或病或不病，或皆病，或皆不病，其故何也？少俞曰：帝问何急？黄帝曰：愿尽间之。少俞曰：春青风，夏阳风，秋凉风，冬寒风。凡此四时之风者，其所病各不同形。

The Yellow Emperor asked Shaoyu: People of the same age wearing similar clothes may be caught in rainstorm while standing or walking together ...

It was fine just now!

Let's run out of it quickly!

Some are taken ill while some are not ...

I was taken ill after running back from the rain.

Sometimes all are taken ill or none are taken ill.

What is the cause?

The different types of seasonal winds may cause different
results depending on the physical conditions of the people involved.

原文：黄帝曰：四时之风，病人如何？少俞曰：黄色薄皮弱肉者，不皮春之虚风；白色薄皮弱肉者，不皮夏之虚风；青色薄皮弱肉，不皮秋之虚风；赤色薄皮弱肉，不皮冬之虚风也。

Shaoyu: People with thin yellowish skin and soft weak muscles are vulnerable to the abnormal wind in spring.

The Yellow Emperor: What kind of people are most vulnerable to the particular type of wind of each season?

Mummy, why do you look like this?

I'm ill from the wind.

People with thin green-bluish skin and soft weak muscles are vulnerable to the abnormal wind in autumn.

People with white thin skin and soft weak muscles are vulnerable to the abnormal wind in summer.

People with thin reddish skin and soft weak muscles are vulnerable to the abnormal wind in winter.

原文：黄帝曰：黑色不病乎？少俞曰
：黑色而皮厚肉坚，固不伤于四时之
风；其皮薄而肉不坚，色不一者，长
夏至而有虚风者，病矣。其皮厚而肌
肉坚者，长夏至而有虚风，不病矣。
其皮厚而肌肉坚者，必重感于寒，外
内皆然，乃病。

The Yellow Emperor: Does it mean people with black skin will not be ill from the wind of the different seasons?

Shaoyu: Thick dark skin and firm muscles are generally manifestations of good health. People with such skin and muscles are generally not vulnerable to the wind in different seasons.

Mummy, your face keeps changing colour.

Dear, I'm not feeling well. Go and play with your Granny.

But some people with thin skin and slack muscles have changing skin colours.

Such people are vulnerable to the abnormal wind in long summer.

If they have thick skin and firm muscles, they will not easily get ill even if exposed to the abnormal wind in long summer.

In some cases people with thick skin and firm muscles are not only attacked by the abnormal wind,

but also invaded by the cold evil, they can hardly avoid falling ill, since both the exterior and the interior of the body are injured.

原文：黄帝曰：夫人忍痛与不忍痛者，非勇怯之分也。夫勇士之不忍痛者，见难则前，见痛则止；夫怯士之忍痛者，闻难则恐，遇痛不动。

Whether a person is brave or timid does not decide his capacity to endure pain.

Some valiant people cannot endure pain. They advance bravely in face of difficulty and danger.

It hurts like anything!

You just have to put up with it!

戰地医院

Field Clinic

But they wince before pain.

Among timid people who are nervous in face of difficulty, there are some who can maintain their composure in the case of pain.

This guy does not fear painful work, but has no courage to go to the battlefield.

原文：夫勇士之忍痛者，见难不恐，遇痛不动；夫怯士之不忍痛者，见难与痛，目转眼盼，恐不能言，失气，惊，颜色变化，乍死乍生。余见其然也，不知其何由，愿闻其故。

There are valiant people who are neither afraid of pain nor difficulty and danger.

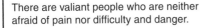

The operation is over.

There are timid people who wince both in the case of pain and in the face of difficulty and danger.

Clonk!

They may be frightened speechless or even out of their wits with their face going pale.

Am I still alive?

It's just the basin that I dropped on the floor out of carelessness.

What are the causes of the above conditions?

163

原文：少俞曰：夫忍痛与不忍痛者，皮肤之薄厚，肌肉之坚脆，缓急之分也，非勇怯之谓也。

Whether one can endure pain mainly depends on the thickness of the skin and the firmness and strength of the muscles and cannot merely be judged from bravery or timidity.

原文：黄帝曰：愿闻勇怯之所由然。

少俞曰：勇士者，目深以固，长冲直扬，三焦理横，其心端直，其肝大以坚，其胆满以傍，怒则气盛而胸胀，肝举而胆横，眦裂而目扬，毛起而面苍，此勇士之由然者也。

Please explain why some people are brave and some are timid.

Shaoyu: Brave people have deep-set bright eyes and upward slanting eyebrows, and they are capable of looking with a fixed piercing gaze.

They have rough skin and stringy muscles, normal heart, large and solid liver, full gallbladder, and abundant bile.

When they get angry, they are imposing and awe-inspiring, with eyes wide open in flashing gaze, hair standing on ends, face showing a green-bluish colour, liver qi rising and gallbladder qi overflowing. That is because the functions of their heart, liver and gallbladder are healthy and strong; the fundamental cause deciding the nature of the brave.

原文：怯士者，目大而不减，阴阳相失，其焦理纵，髑骺短而小，肝系缓，其胆不满而纵，肠胃挺，胁下空，虽方大怒，气不能满其胸，肝肺虽举，气衰复下，故不能久怒，此怯士之所由然者也。

愿闻怯士之所由然。

Then please explain the nature of the timid and the underlying cause.

The timid have large but dull eyes and there is a lack of flexibility in the movement of the eyeballs.

Is that me?

The blood and qi are out of harmony, the muscles are slack and hardly visible, and the xyphoid of the chest bone is short and small.

The liver is slack, the gallbladder long and drooping without sufficient bile, and the intestines thin and straight without enough windings.

The liver qi below the ribs is not abundant enough, and the qi of rage will not fill up the chest even though the person bursts into anger.

Even if the liver qi and the lung qi are stimulated and raised ...

... they will not be able to last but will soon decline and disperse.

How disappointing!

So the rage will not persist, and that is the fundamental cause deciding the nature of the timid.

酒者，水谷之精，熟谷之液也，其气剽悍，其入于胃中，则胃胀，气上逆，满于胸中，肝浮胆横，当是之时，固此于勇士，气衰则悔。与勇士同类，不知避之，名曰酒悖也。

怯士之得酒，怒不避勇士着，和脏使然？

After the timid people drink alcohol, they will be as brave and reckless as valiants.

I dare not, I dare not.

If you dare to curse me again!

What function makes them behave like that?

Being the essence of grains and water through fermentation, alcohol is strong and violent by nature.

When it gets into the stomach, it will distend the organ and make the qi flow upward to fill up the chest.

Bullshit!

168

Treatise on the Five Flavours

原文：五谷：粳米甘、麻酸、大豆咸、麦苦、黄黍辛。五果：枣甘、李酸、栗咸、杏苦、桃辛。五畜：牛甘、犬酸、猪咸、羊苦、鸡辛。五菜：葵甘、韭酸、藿咸、薤苦、葱辛。

What are the five flavours?

Different types of grains, fruits, animal meat, and vegetables have different flavours which are each conducive to people suffering from diseases of different organs who should therefore eat more of a particular flavour. Each organ has an aversion to a particular flavour, so patients of that organ should avoid that flavour.

Please explain to me the five flavours.

Bogao: Among the grains:

Rice

粳米

rice is sweet

Sesame

芝麻

sesame is sour

大豆

Soy Bean

soy bean is salty

millet

黄黍

millet is pungent

Wheat

麦

wheat is bitter

Allow me to make further explanations:

Among the fruits:

plum is sour

chestnut is salty

apricot is bitter

date is sweet

peach is pungent

原文：五宜所言五色者，脾病者，宜食粳米饭、牛肉枣葵；心病者，宜食麦羊肉杏薤；肾病者，宜食大豆黄卷猪肉栗藿；肝病者，宜食麻犬肉李韭；肺病者，宜食黄黍鸡肉桃葱。

The five proprieties refer to dietary requirements by people suffering from the diseases of a particular organ. Sweet flavour is conducive to those suffering from spleen disease who should therefore eat more rice, beef, date, and kui vegetable.

Bitter flavour is conducive to people with heart disease who should eat more wheat, beef, apricot, and wild garlic.

Mutton
Apricot
Wheat
Wild Garlic

Salty flavour is conducive to people with kidney disease who should eat more bean sprouts, pork, chestnut, and bean leaf.

Pork
Bean Sprouts
Bean Leaf
Chestnut

Sesame
Dog meat
Plum
Leek

Sour flavour is conducive to people with liver disease who should eat more sesame, dog meat, plum, and leek.

Pungent flavour is conducive to people with lung disease who should eat more millet, chicken, peach, and onion.

Chicken
Millet
Onion
Peach

172

原文：肝病禁辛，心病禁咸，脾病禁酸
，肾病禁甘，肺病禁苦。

Disease of each organ has its particular contra-indication.

The liver is associated with wood and liver disease which contra-indicates the pungent flavour associated with metal. Metal overwhelms wood.

The heart is associated with fire and heart disease which contra-indicates the salty flavour associated with water. Water overwhelms fire.

The doctor has advised you to avoid eating onion.

Pork is salty by nature. Better avoid eating it.

腊肉

Sesame, plum, leek and dog meat are all sour by nature.

The kidneys are associated with water and kidney disease which contra-indicates sweet flavour associated with earth. Earth overwhelms water.

Take away the beef and the kui vegetable. I won't eat them.

Be sure to keep in mind the above advice of the doctor.

The spleen is associated with earth and spleen disease which contra-indicates the sour flavour associated with wood. Wood overwhelms earth.

The lungs are associated with metal and lung disease which contra-indicates the bitter flavour associated with fire. Fire overwhelms metal.

173

Treatise on the Origin of Diseases

Sudden overeating and irregular living habits or overexertion of the body will injure the collaterals. In the case of injury to the collaterals of the intestines, blood will flow out of the intestines congealing with the juice and foam of the cold evil. The congelation will linger and expand, forming accumulation disease.

原文：卒然多食饮则肠满，起居不节，用力过度则络脉伤。阳络伤则血外溢，血外溢则衄血，阴络伤则血内溢，血内溢则后血。肠胃之络伤，则血溢于肠外，肠外有寒汁沫与血相搏，则并合凝聚不得散，而积成矣。

Sudden over-eating will distend the stomach and intestines.

That coupled with an irregular daily life or overexertion of the body will injure the collaterals.

174

Injury to yang collaterals will cause the outward overflow of the blood resulting in spontaneous external bleeding.

Injury to the yin collaterals will cause the inward overflow of the blood resulting in blood in the stool.

Injury to the collaterals of the stomach and intestines will result in blood flowing out of the intestines.

In case there is cold evil outside the intestines, its juice and foam will congeal with the outflowing blood. The congelation will linger and expand gradually forming accumulation disease.

175

176

If the wind evil goes reversely upward from the feet, the result will be soreness in the feet and impediment to movement.

It will also cause a feeling of chill in the feet and shanks resulting in stagnation of blood circulation in this part of the body.

The cold evil may go further upward into the intestines and the stomach.

The invasion of cold evil into the intestines and the stomach will affect the transformation and movement of grain and water resulting in abdomen distention

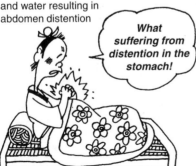

It will also cause congelation of cold evil and the juice and foams outside the intestines which will linger and result in accumulation disease.

原文：卒然外中于寒，若内伤于忧怒，则气上逆，气上逆则六俞不通，温气不行，凝血蕴里而不散，津液涩渗。著而不去，而积皆成矣。

It means I have to sleep in the open tonight and I haven't got a blanket.

Sometimes one may be suddenly invaded by cold evil.

That coupled with sorrow or anger will make the qi flow reversely upward.

Where has my friend moved?

Very far, but he didn't tell me exactly.

The reverse upward flow of qi will stagnate the transportation of the channel qi and hinder the smooth flow of yang qi resulting in the congelation of blood.

I have even run out of money for my journey back.

The movement of fluids will also be affected, which will, over time, result in the accumulation disease.

Oh, what suffering!

Treatise on the Classification of People

Based on yin-yang and the five elements, people are classified into five categories: the greater yin type are greedy and treacherous; the lesser yin type lack sympathy and tend to take advantage of others; the greater yang type are braggarts of their ability and ambition but never carry anything through; the lesser yang type are conceited, good at socializing but not good at their own jobs. Harmonious yin and yang follow the natural ways of things and have no greed or excessive joy.

原文：黄帝问于少师曰：余尝闻人有阴阳，何谓阴人？何谓阳人？少师曰：天地之间，六合之内，不离于五，人亦应之，非徒一阴一阳而已也，而略言耳，口弗能遍明也。黄帝曰：愿略闻其意，有贤人圣人，心能备而行之乎？少师曰：盖有太阴之人，少阴之人，太阳之人，少阳之人，阴阳和平之人。凡五人者，其态不同，其筋骨气血各不等。

I hear people are classified into different types: some belong to yin and some belong to yang. How is that?

179

The classification of all things in the universe are generally associated with the five elements.

The classification of people are also closely related to the five elements instead of an oversimplified classification into two opposite types of yin and yang.

You rude boy!

Why? The boy is not so rude at usual times.

The different natural endowments of different types of people are too complicated to explain in just a few words.

Please give me some general idea of the relevant implications. Are all the sages and men of virtue well balanced in yin and yang? Is this harmony of yin and yang manifested in their behaviour?

Generally speaking, there are five types of people: people belonging to the greater yin;

people belonging to the lesser yin;

How happy I am! That guy is going to get it in the neck.

people belonging to the greater yang;

I'm second to none in the world.

people belonging to the lesser yang; and people of well-balanced and harmonious yin and yang.

The local government has appointed me secretary.

....
....

The above five types are different from each other in shape, strength of bone and muscle and exuberance of qi and blood.

181

原文：黄帝曰：其不等者，可得闻乎？少师曰：太阴之人，贪而不仁，下齐湛湛，好内而恶出，心和而不发，不务于时，动而后之，此太阴之人也。

Will you please explain the various differences between the five types of people?

Those belonging to a greater yin are greedy and cruel. They have a treacherous mind behind a modest facade.

What a bum?

Master Li is ready to help other and grants whatever is asked.

But the interest we have to pay is too high.

Their remarks and behaviour do not reveal their true thoughts. They go with the current in making decisions and are always hesitant before the trend of things becomes manifest.

What's the hurry? Just wait and see.

Master, the grain market is expected to rise. What shall we do?

Such treacherous people with honest appearance belong to the greater yin category.

182

 原文：少阴之人，小贪而贼心，见人有亡，常若有得，好伤好害，见人有荣，乃反愠怒，心疾而无恩，此少阴之人也。

Those belonging to lesser yin covet petty gains and are preoccupied with taking advantages of others.

Why? One steamed bread is missing.

What a fool! He's still in the dark.

They will gloat over the losses sustained by others just as if they had gained something themselves.

+ − x ÷

Don't you know Young Lie lost a lot of money just in one deal?

What a poor guy!

They tend to harm people and to be jealous of others, fretting over their successes and glory.

Oh, I've got it right at last. I have made a nice sum of money instead of losing any.

Besides, they have no sympathy for others and are cruel in nature. Such greedy and cruel people who take pleasure in others' misfortune belong to lesser yin.

Simply want to burn his store ...

原文：太阳之人，居处于于，好言大事，无能而虚说，志法于四野，举措不顾是非，为事如常自用，事虽败，而常无悔，此太阳之人也。

Those belonging to greater yang are not very particular about the place they live in and would make their home wherever they go. They like to talk big whereas their ability is actually limited.

Leave everything to me! I'll defeat the enemy without fail.

I'll make you the chief general.

Being boastful they like to brag about their ambition to everyone.

He is in great danger.

Your son has received the order.

They are rude and reckless and are often over-confident of their own mediocrity. They would show no sign of repentance even if they are defeated.

It's all your fault.

These boastful people who never carry anything through belong to the category of greater yang.

原文：阴阳和平之人，居处安静，无为惧惧，无为欣欣，婉然从物，或与不争，与时变化，尊则谦谦，谭而不治，是谓至治。

People of a well-balanced and harmonious yin and yang live a regular quiet life with a tranquil frame of mind.

Quite right.

A cat plus a dog equals a chicken plus a duck.

They give little thought to personal gains or losses, and adapt their life to the change of seasons.

Since the harvest is poor, you don't have to pay full tuition fees.

I'm so sorry, but I'll do my best for the payment.

Without fear or greed or excessive joy, they follow the natural development of things.

Even though in high position, they remain modest and prefer to govern the people through persuasion instead of solely resorting to regulations and punishment.

That is "ideal government" as people call it.

Treatise on Confusion

The eyes are the confluence of essence qi. An unexpected terrifying sight will give rise to sight confusion, and the invasion of evil qi may cause a distorted vision. Sudden vision disturbance will make one puzzled or even confounded. Insufficiency of qi in the heart and lungs and clogging of qi in the stomach and intestines will cause forgetfulness.

原文：目者，五脏六腑之精也，营卫魂魄之所常营也，神气之所生也。故神劳则魂魄散，志意乱。是故瞳子黑眼法于阴，白眼赤脉法于阳也，故阴阳合传而精明也。目者，心使也。心者，神之舍也，故神精乱而不转。卒然见非常处，精神魂魄，散不相得，故曰惑也。

The eyes are where the essence of qi of the viscera converges, where the nourishing qi and defence qi as well as the ethereal soul and the corporeal soul operate, and where the spiritual activities manifest themselves.

If one is spiritually too tired, his ethereal and corporeal soul will get dispersed, leading to confusion of the mind and will.

The eye is governed by the heart spirit and the heart is in charge of consciousness and thinking.

The pupil is governed by the essence of qi in the liver and the kidneys. The white of the eye and the red vessels are governed by the essence of qi in the heart and the lungs. The eyes are bright as a result of the convergence of various essence of qi.

The confusion of the heart spirit will cause failure in the convergence of the various essence of qi. Unexpected alarm and terrifying sights will lead to failure in coordination between the spirit, the ethereal and corporeal soul whose dispersion will give rise to sight confusion.

原文：五脏六腑之精气，皆上注于目而为之精。精之窠为眼，骨之精为瞳子，筋之精为黑眼，血之精为络，其窠气之精为白眼，肌肉之精为约束，裹撷筋骨血气之精而与脉并为系，上属于脑，后出于项中。故邪中于项，因逢其身之虚，其入深，则随眼系以入于脑，入于脑则脑转，脑转则引目系急，目系急则目眩以转矣。邪其精，其精所中不相比也，则精散，精散则视岐，视岐见两物。

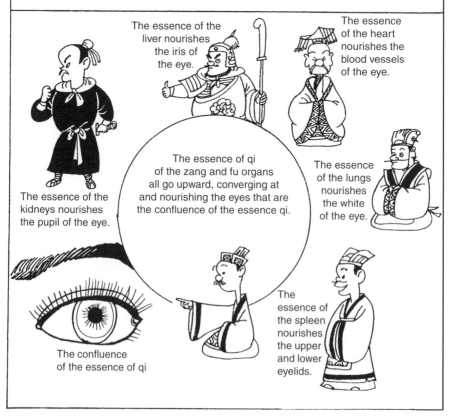

The essence of the liver nourishes the iris of the eye.

The essence of the heart nourishes the blood vessels of the eye.

The essence of the kidneys nourishes the pupil of the eye.

The essence of qi of the zang and fu organs all go upward, converging at and nourishing the eyes that are the confluence of the essence qi.

The essence of the lungs nourishes the white of the eye.

The confluence of the essence of qi

The essence of the spleen nourishes the upper and lower eyelids.

The Essence of Tendons, Bones, Blood and Qi combines with the Vessels and Networks forming the Eye Tie.

黄帝曰：余疑其然，余每之东苑，未曾不惑，去之则复，余唯独为东苑劳神乎？何其异也？
岐伯曰：不然也。心有所喜，神有所恶，卒然相惑，则精气乱，视误，故惑，神移乃复。是故间者为迷，甚者为惑。

The Yellow Emperor: I become puzzled and confounded whenever I am in the East Garden but feel normal again when I am out of it.

Is this the north gate?

No, Your Majesty. This is the south gate.

Is it because my spirit is heavily taxed only when I am in the Garden? Why should I have such an abnormal experience?

Qibo: That's not the case. The mind undergoes different moods of delight and anger. A sudden change of mood will dissipate the essence of qi and cause vision disturbance.

As a result, one will become puzzled in a minor case and confounded in a serious one. However, things will be normal again when one's attention is away from the source of confusion. That is why you feel well again when you are out of the Garden.

原文：黄帝曰：人之善忘者，何气使然？岐伯曰：上气不足，下气有余，肠胃实而心肺虚，虚则营卫留于下，久之不以时上，故善忘也。

The Yellow Emperor: What is the cause for forgetfulness?

That's interesting, looking for the donkey while riding on it.

Where's my donkey?

Qibo: That is the result of insufficiency in the upper qi coupled with surplus in the lower qi, i.e. overaccumulation of qi in the stomach and intestines and insufficiency of qi in the heart and lungs.

Why is it like this?

It's because of the clogging of qi in the stomach and intestines.

We have to stay here in the stomach and intestines as the heart and lungs are too weak.

Vacuity and weakness of the heart and the lungs will result in accumulation of the nourishing qi and defence qi in the stomach and intestines.

Oh, no! I even forgot I was just riding on the donkey.

Prolonged stagnation of the qi in the stomach and intestines will cause failure to transport the qi upward, resulting in forgetfulness.

 原文：人之善饥而不迫食者，何气使然？岐伯曰：精气并于脾，热气留于胃，胃热则消谷，谷消故善饥。胃气逆上，则胃脘寒。故不迫食也。

The Yellow Emperor: Why is it that some people have no appetite while they feel hungry?

I'm so hungry but don't feel like eating.

Qibo: Failure to transport the essence of qi accumulated in the spleen will cause clogging of heat qi in the stomach.

精氣

Essence qi

Get me my meal!

The stomach

胃

Depressed heat in the stomach will digest the food, resulting in the feeling of hunger.

Now I see the reason.

The reverse upward flow of the stomach qi will clog the stomach duct resulting in loss of appetite.

Appendix: The 13 Prescriptions - Undecanted Wine Decoction

Acupuncture is the major means of treatment in the *Yellow Emperor's Medicine Classic* and only 13 prescriptions are mentioned in it. Though limited in number, the 13 prescriptions are the earliest records of therapy with medicines. Some of them are still of clinical significance today and are selected here for reference.

内经中的治疗，多以针法为主，对方药的运用
，仅提出了十三个，一般称为"十三方"。十三
方方药虽少，但却是我国最早运用方药治疗疾
病的记载，而且其中的某些方剂，现今临床上
仍有一定的意义，先将其选绘于后。

The Yellow Emperor: How and why is laoli or undecanted wine prepared from the five grains?

原文：黄帝问曰：为五谷汤液及醪醴，奈何？岐伯
曰：必以稻米，炊之稻薪，稻米者完，稻薪者坚。
帝曰：何以然？岐伯曰：此得天地之和，高下之宜
，故能至完；伐取得时，故能至坚也。

Note: In ancient times, laoli was made by boiling the grains for a long time before fermentation. Such undecanted wine is used for treatment of diseases in the viscera.

Qibo: The rice which is abundant in qi is boiled with rice straw for fuel which is tough and strong. Nourished with the harmonious qi of heaven and earth and growing in fields neither too high nor too low, the plant is enriched with qi. It is harvested in autumn and has strong and tough straw.

Qibo

Iron Flakes Beverage

帝曰：有病怒狂者，⋯⋯治之奈何？岐伯曰：⋯⋯使之服以生铁为饮。夫生铁者，下气疾也。

The Yellow Emperor: What is the way to treat a frenzied patient?

What's that?

Take the beverage and you'll get well.

Qibo: The iron flakes beverage will cure him as it has the effect of lowering the qi and opening the binding.

Note: The iron flakes beverage is prepared by grinding in water flakes from striking hot iron.

It is effective for phlegm-fire caused by decocting the fluids by the depressed fire resulting from stagnation of the qi of the liver injured by violent rage. In recent times, it has been more effective to administer it with adjuvants that help transform phlegm and open the orifices.

Hair Powder Liquor

原文：邪客于手足少阴太阴足阳明之络，以五络皆会于耳中，上络左角，五络俱竭，令人身脉皆动，而无形知也，其状若尸，或曰片厥⋯⋯鬄其左角之发，方一寸，燔治，饮以美酒一杯，不能饮者，灌之，立已。

The network vessels of the five channels of foot greater yin, hand greater yin, foot lesser yin, hand lesser yin, and foot yang brightness all meet in the ear. The evil qi that has penetrated into the network vessels of the five channels will travel along to the frontal angle above the left ear where the network vessels meet. The channels of the whole body will be shaken if the qi of all the five channels is debilitated.

In this case, the body will lose consciousness and lie corpse-like. This is also known as "deathlike reversal".

In case acupuncture is ineffective, cut off the hair of the patient at his left frontal angle for a patch a bit larger than 1 square inch.

Burn the hair in fire before grinding it into powder.

If the patient has completely lost consciousness and is therefore unable to take medicine, pour the hair powder in with good liquor and the patient will be out of danger immediately.

Alisma Decoction

原文：有病身热解堕，汗出如浴，恶风少气，此为何病？岐伯曰：病名曰酒风。帝曰：治之奈何？岐伯曰：以泽泻、术各十分，麋衔五分，合以三指撮为后饭。

The Yellow Emperor: There is a case that the patient has a fever all over with limp limbs and excessive sweating.

Have you just taken a bath?

What's wrong with me after all?

The patient is vulnerable to wind, and is short of breath with inhibited respiration. What is the illness and how should it be treated?

Qibo: This is called jiufeng (literally meaning liquor wind). Get 5 grams of alisma, 5 grams of ovate atractylodes, and 2.5 grams of mixian to be ground into powder. Use about 3 pinches of it before meals.

Alisma has a bland percolating water-disinhibiting effect and damp-heat, clearing effect. Ovate atractylodes is warm and bitter by nature and has a dampness drying and perspiration checking effect. Mixian is a kind of medicine for rheumatism.

Chicken Dropping Wine

原文：黄帝问曰：有病心腹满，旦食则不能暮食，此为何病？岐伯对曰：名为鼓胀。帝曰：治之奈何？岐伯曰：治之以鸡矢醴，一剂知，二剂已。

The Yellow Emperor: There is a kind of distention in the stomach and abdomen. The patient is not able to have any more food even towards evening after having a meal early in the morning. What is the illness and how to cure it?

I don't feel like eating.

Qibo: The disease is called drum distention which can be cured with two preparations of chicken dropping wine.

Bake white chicken droppings that has been dried in the sun till it turns yellow. Mix 50 grams of the chicken droppings with three bowls of rice wine. Boil the mixture several times before removing the dregs by filtering. Wait till it has settled and drink it hot twice a day on an empty stomach.

Good, you've fully recovered.

The nature of chicken droppings is capable of dispersing accumulation and directing the qi down as well as freeing urine and stool. It is indeed a conqueror of repletion evil.

Zhang Jingyue

Pill of Cuttlefish Bone and Madder

原文：帝曰：有病胸胁支满者，妨于食，病至则先闻腥臊臭，出清液，先唾血，四支清，目眩，时时前后血，病名为何？何以得知？岐伯曰：病名血枯。此得之年少有所大脱血；若醉入房中，气竭肝伤，故月事衰少不来也。帝曰：治之奈何？复以何术？岐伯曰：以四乌鲗骨、一藘茹二物并合之，丸以雀卵，大如小豆；以五丸为后饭，饮以鲍鱼汁，利肠中及伤肝也。

The Yellow Emperor: There is a kind of distention in the chest and rib-side that affects eating and is preluded with a fishy and animal breath.

Mom, there is a foul smell from your mouth.

Is that so?

The patient may have clear water upflow or may even vomit blood. The limbs will gradually get cold, the eyes will have distorted vision, and blood will be found in the urine and stool. What is the name of the disease and what is the cause?

Oh!

Is there blood?

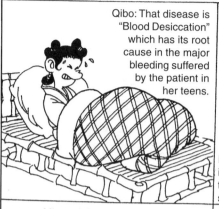

Qibo: That disease is "Blood Desiccation" which has its root cause in the major bleeding suffered by the patient in her teens.

It's quite right.

It may also have resulted from sexual intercourse after getting drunk which depletes the essence of qi and injures the liver, causing scant menstruation or even menstrual block.

Mix cuttlefish bone powder (constituting four fifths) and madder (constituting one fifth) with sparrow egg and roll the mixture into pills the size of beans.

The medicine is quite effective.

Mom is so brave.

Take 5 pills before meals with juice from boiled abalone which clears the intestines and supplements the injured liver.

The pill also supplements semen, qi and blood, strengthens the lungs, the liver, the kidneys, and quickens blood circulation and eases menstruation. Therefore, it is effective for blood desiccation and semen depletion.

Note: Cuttlefish bone is salty and warm, effective for red and white vaginal discharge. Madder is sweet and cold, capable of stanching blood and curing flooding, as well as harmonizing the blood and freeing menstruation. Sparrow egg is sweet and warm, and can supplement semen and blood, curing impotence and vaginal discharge, as well as constipation and rough urination. Abalone is acrid and warm and can free the blood and supplement the yin qi. And the juice from boiling abalone, taken with other medicines, clears clotted blood.

Forsythia Drink

原文：发于胁，名曰败疵，女子病也。灸之其病大痈脓。治之其中乃有生肉，大如赤小豆。锉连翘草根各一升，以水一斗六升煮之，竭为取三升，则强饮，厚衣，坐于釜上，冷汗出至足，已。

The pains in the rib-side of a woman cannot be cured by way of acupuncture which will cause ulceration in such a case. Growths of flesh the size of beans are found on close examination.

Get one litre each of forsythia leaf and root to be put in 16 liters of water for boiling and simmering till 3 litres of the mixture is left. Drink the medicine at one go before sitting in a steamer in heavy clothes. The patient will be cured after a good sweating.

Note: Bitter and mildly cold, forsythia has the effect of draining the fever fire of the two channels of the heart and liver, reducing heat and resolving toxin, and clearing welling abscess and dissipating stagnation. All types of sores are associated with the heart. And forsythia is an effective medicine for sores.

Examples of Moral Cultivation

Overcoming Joy with Fright

Overcoming Obsession with Anger

It is recorded in *"Comments On Ancient And Contemporary Medical Cases"* that a famous doctor Zhu Danxi once treated a woman whose husband had been away from home on business for 20 years.

Longing for her husband, she lost appetite and became dull and inactive as if dumb and stupid and no medicine showed any effect.

What can I do?

Medicine alone will not cure her.

May I ask ...

After examining the patient, the doctor Zhu Danxi told her father that she had a qi binding as a result of prolonged obsession and was to be treated with psycho therapy instead of with medicine alone.

Following the instruction of the doctor, her father gave her a few slaps on the face accompanied with loud scolding. The patient was very angry for that and yelled in tears.

I'll beat you to death!

Help! Help!

Then the patient began to eat after taking some medicine prescribed by the doctor who later bid her father to tell her that a letter had been received from her husband that he was coming back home before long.

Your husband is coming back soon.

Is that so? Great!

Her condition improved day by day after that and never relapsed.

Child, come join me for lunch!

Overcoming Sorrow with Joy

The young scholar burst out laughing.

What a quack! Can't even tell a man from a woman! Famous doctor indeed!

After that, he could not help laughing whenever he thought of the doctor. And he often told other people about this funny experience so that they could have a good laugh.

Ridiculous!

What's the use of such a quack?

Being in a good mood, the young scholar gradually recovered over time and his appetite greatly improved.

Mama, I have gotten well without taking any medicine.

You should go to the doctor and express your thanks without delay.

It was only then that his mother told him the doctor's approach of overcoming sorrow with joy.

Overcoming Worry with Anger

It was recorded in *"The History Of The Three Kingdoms"* how the famous doctor Hua Tuo treated a magistrate who had been gloomy and depressed as a result of prolonged illness.

> I'm afraid I won't be able to get well again.

> The doctor is here.

After examining the patient, Hua Tuo decided to apply psychotherapy to cure his illness by making him angry.

> What we have to do is just ...

> How can you serve such poor wine? Don't you want me to cure you?

So Hua Tuo stayed in the home of the magistrate, eating and drinking extravagantly, and demanding a lot of gold and silver but without doing anything towards his illness.

> The doctor says you are a corrupt official.

The magistrate got very angry. Later, Hua Tuo simply sneaked away without even saying good-bye, but he left an abusive letter behind.

209

Overcoming Excessive Joy with Grief

There was an example in a medicine book of the Qing Dynasty about overcoming excessive joy with grief. Li Dajian, a young man from a long line of peasants, passed the provincial examination.

Old Li, your son has passed the provincial examination!

What? I beg your pardon!

The young man's father kept laughing for joy.

Ha! Ha! Is it true? Is it true?

Will you please allow me to be your servant?

Yes, my lord.

Later, the young man passed the national examination and became a senior official. His father was all the more overjoyed and kept laughing day and night for 10 years before a court doctor was sent to treat his stubborn illness.

Overcoming Rage with Joy

It is recorded in the chapter "Seven Emotional Factors" of the book *"Ancient And Present Medical Cases"* how doctor Zhang Zihe treated the wife of Xiang Guanling who had been in a constant rage, yelling and shouting at people, unable to eat though hungry.

What are her symptoms?

The mistress used to be kind and generous.

You cursed! Wait till I break your neck!

As she was not cured after prolonged treatment, Zhang Zihe was sent to have a try.

Zhang bade the husband to get two women made up in a funny way to put on an amusing performance for his wife.

Come, darling. There is an exciting performance.

213

Hilarious Chinese Classics by Tsai Chih Chung

Journey to the West 1

These books offer more than the all-too-familiar escapades of Tan Sanzang and his animal disciples. Under the creative pen of Tsai Chih Chung, *Journey to the West* still stays its course but takes a new route. En route from ancient China to India to acquire Buddhist scriptures, the Monk and his disciples veer off course frequently to dart into modern times to have fleeting exchanges with characters ranging from Ronald Reagan to Bunny Girls of the Playboy Club.

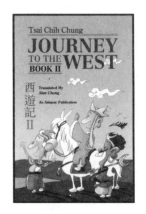

Journey to the West 2

Romance of the Three Kingdoms

Set in the turbulent Three Kingdoms Period, *Romance of the Three Kingdoms* relates the clever political manoeuvres and brilliant battle strategies used by the ambitious rulers as they fought one another for supremacy.

In this comic version, Tsai Chih Chung has illustrated in an entertaining way the four best-known episodes in the novel. Don't be surprised to see a warrior waving an Iraqi flag, a satellite dish fixed on top of an ancient Chinese building, and court officials playing mahjong or eating beef noodles, a favourite Taiwanese snack.

Strategy & Leadership Series by Wang Xuanming

Thirty-six Stratagems: Secret Art of War
Translated by Koh Kok Kiang (cartoons) &
Liu Yi (text of the stratagems)
 A Chinese military classic which emphasizes deceptive schemes to achieve military objectives. It has attracted the attention of military authorities and general readers alike.

Six Strategies for War: The Practice of Effective Leadership
Translated by Alan Chong
 A powerful book for rulers, administrators and leaders, it covers critical areas in management and warfare including: how to recruit talents and manage the state; how to beat the enemy and build an empire; how to lead wisely; and how to manoeuvre brilliantly.

Gems of Chinese Wisdom: Mastering the Art of Leadership
Translated by Leong Weng Kam
 Wise up with this delightful collection of tales and anecdotes on the wisdom of great men and women in Chinese history, including Confucius, Meng Changjun and Gou Jian.

Three Strategies of Huang Shi Gong: The Art of Government
Translated by Alan Chong
 Reputedly one of man's oldest monograph on military strategy, it unmasks the secrets behind brilliant military manoeuvres, clever deployment and control of subordinates, and effective government.

100 Strategies of War: Brilliant Tactics in Action
Translated by Yeo Ai Hoon
 The book captures the essence of extensive military knowledge and practice, and explores the use of psychology in warfare, the importance of building diplomatic relations with the enemy's neighbours, the use of espionage and reconnaissance, etc.

Latest Titles in
Strategy & Leadership Series

Chinese Business Strategies

The Chinese are known for being shrewd businessmen able to thrive under the toughest market conditions. The secret of their success lies in 10 time-tested principles of Chinese entrepreneurship.

This book offers readers 30 real-life, ancient case studies with comments on their application in the context of modern business.

Sixteen Strategies of Zhuge Liang

Zhuge Liang, the legendary statesman and military commander during the Three Kingdoms Period, is the epitome of wisdom.

Well-grounded in military principles of Sun Zi and other masters before him, he excelled in applying them in state administration and his own innovations, thus winning many spectacular victories with his uncanny anticipation of enemy moves.

SPECIAL OFFER

Strategy & Leadership Series

☐ Chinese Business Strategies
☐ Three Strategies of Huang Shi Gong
☐ Six Strategies for War
☐ Sixteen Strategies of Zhuge Liang
☐ Thirty-six Stratagems
☐ 100 Strategies of War
☐ Gems of Chinese Wisdom

Make your subscription for any 5 volumes or more of this comic series (tick box) and enjoy **20% discount**.
Original Price: S$15.90 per volume (*exclusive* of GST)
Offer at special discount (*inclusive of* postage):-

	5 Volumes	6 Volumes	7 Volumes
Singapore	68.30	82.20	95.30
Malaysia	71.60	88.30	101.00
International-by sea mail	78.60	100.30	113.00

* All Prices in Singapore Dollars. 3% GST charge for local orders.

I wish to subscribe for the above-mentioned titles

at the nett price of **S$**_____ (*inclusive of* postage)

☐ *For Singapore orders only:*
   Enclosed is my postal order/money order/cheque/ for **S$** _____

   (No.: _____)

   For Singapore/Malaysia/International orders:

☐ Credit card. Please charge the amount of SIN$_____ to my credit card

VISA ☐ Card No. _____ Card Holder's Name _____

MASTER ☐ Expiry Date_____ Order Date_____ Signature _____

Name _____

Address _____

_____ **Tel** _____

Send to: ASIAPAC BOOKS PTE LTD 629 Aljunied Road #04-06 Cititech Industrial Building
         Singapore 389838 Tel: 65 -7453868 Fax: 65 -7453822
Note:
For this offer of 20% discount, there is no restriction on the titles ordered, that is, you may order any 5 or more of the series. Prices are subject to change without prior notice.

≪亞太漫畫系列≫

黃帝內經
養生圖典

編文：周春才
繪畫：周春才、韓亞洲、
　　　韓軼、候秀清
翻譯：王學文、隨雲

亞太圖書有限公司出版